Met. O. 1016

METEOROLOGICAL OFFICE

THE
MARINE OBSERVER'S
HANDBOOK

11TH EDITION

LONDON: HMSO

Applications for reproduction should be made to HMSO Copyright Unit
Eleventh Edition 1995

ISBN 0 11 400367 X

Published by HMSO and available from:

HMSO Publications Centre
(Mail, fax and telephone orders only)
PO Box 276, London, SW8 5DT
Telephone orders 0171-873 9090
General enquiries 0171-873 0011
(queuing system in operation for both numbers)
Fax orders 0171-873 8200

HMSO Bookshops
49 High Holborn, London, WC1V 6HB
(counter service only)
0171-873 0011 Fax 0171-831 1326
68–69 Bull Street, Birmingham, B4 6AD
0121-236 9696 Fax 0121-236 9699
33 Wine Street, Bristol, BS1 2BQ
0117-926 4306 Fax 0117-929 4515
9–21 Princess Street, Manchester, M60 8AS
0161-834 7201 Fax 0161-833 0634
16 Arthur Street, Belfast, BT1 4GD
01232 238451 Fax 01232 235401
71 Lothian Road, Edinburgh, EH3 9AZ
0131-228 4181 Fax 0131-229 2734

HMSO's Accredited Agents
(see Yellow Pages)

CONTENTS

iii

CONTENTS — *continued*

Tables

APPENDICES

ILLUSTRATIONS

FOREWORD

The *Marine Observer's Handbook* is written for three purposes:

(1)   To assist officers aboard United Kingdom vessels, who voluntarily make observations at sea on behalf of Meteorological Services, to carry out this work in an efficient and uniform manner.

(2)   To encourage all mariners to take an interest in recording observations of (a) meteorology, (b) marine phenomena and wild life, (c) optical phenomena, and (d) basic oceanography, and to assist them in their study of these important and interesting subjects.

(3)   To provide a book of reference for candidates for Certificates of Competency issued by MSA, the Marine Safety Agency of the Department of Transport.

It will be noted that this book deals with meteorological instruments and the practical aspect of making observations. The companion volume, entitled *Meteorology for Mariners*, embraces the theory and the application of meteorology to the seaman's profession.

The seaman is so dependent on the weather that an interest in meteorology on his part is essential for the safe and economic operation of his ship. It is undoubtedly true that in this modern age of large, fast, power-driven ships, just as in the days of sailing ships, no ship's officer can consider himself a complete mariner unless he is 'weather wise'. Meteorological observing tends to quicken the eye of the observer, making him more alert and more ready for emergencies. The practised observer is not only on the look-out for changes in weather and cloud and for interesting phenomena, but by his general alertness he will ensure that there are no 'Irish pennants', loose lashings, etc., when he is on deck.

Essentials to efficiency in all marine observations are accuracy and attention to detail. The results are beneficial not only to Meteorological Services, the scientific community, and therefore to mankind, but also to the ship herself. By accurate reading and intelligent interpretation of humidity observations, for example, the master can decide whether ventilation of cargo is wise or not, or by a combination of sea and air temperature and humidity, the likelihood of fog can be forecast aboard the ship. Timely notice of a shift of the wind or variation of its force or the sky becoming overcast or gradual deterioration of visibility may, on occasions, save a ship from getting into difficulties. The largest and most powerful ship can be delayed or damaged by rough seas or slowed down in fog. Valuable cargoes can be quickly ruined if due regard is not paid to unfavourable weather.

Anything that is worth doing is worth doing well and this is particularly so with regard to meteorological observations. A lone ship's observation from 'somewhere in the ocean' may hold the key to an otherwise obscure meteorological situation, but it is better to have no observation than an inaccurate or erroneous one. An inaccurate observation may mislead the forecaster and, directly or indirectly as a result of that inaccuracy, an incorrect forecast can cause a small ship or aircraft to set out when a slight change of plan might lead to a smoother and safer passage.

Accuracy is just as important for climatological purposes. In the analysis of meteorological records for the compilation of atlases and for scientific investigation generally, a few inaccurate observations may so bias the results as to tend to falsify the picture. In deciding whether to reject an apparently erroneous observation, the investigator can only use his judgement and experience.

Observers at sea would perhaps be surprised at the many uses to which their observations are put, both commercially and scientifically. To mention only a few: frequencies of winds of gale force are required whenever the load line areas are reviewed; air temperatures and humidities have been useful in the testing of lifejackets; meteorological data are needed by the respective research organizations in connection with the design of ships, with the efficiency of radar and with the issue of global climate change.

Thus, by taking an intelligent interest in all types of marine observation, the seaman contributes to the cause of science and benefits the world in general, and his fellow seamen in particular, by increasing our knowledge of meteorology, climatology and life on the oceans.

Note to the eleventh edition. The tenth edition has been extensively updated and refined, particularly in respect of instrumentation used in weather observing. The section on mercurial barometers has been condensed to reflect the comprehensive adoption of the precision aneroid barometer by the World's Voluntary Observing Fleets. This is reflected in a reduction in the number of correction tables included. In addition, the mercury barometer is no longer a requirement for the UK Department of Transport examinations.

The use of nautical miles and knots, and references to cloud heights in feet, continue to be the exceptions to the metric system. The term hectopascal (hPa) is synonymous with millibar (mb), which is used here as the unit of pressure: the two terms have identical values. The Ice section has been updated in accordance with the latest World Meteorological Organization nomenclature. All chapters have been revised and augmented to include the latest information.

We are indebted to the following for advice and additional text: Commander M.B. Casement, OBE, RN, and Captain P.W.G. Chilman, both of the Royal Naval Birdwatching Society; Dr F. Evans, formerly of the Dove Marine Laboratory, Cullercoats; Dr D. Gavine, Edinburgh; Dr P.J. Herring, Institute of Oceanographic Sciences Deacon Laboratory; Mr R.J. Livesey, British Astronomical Association Aurora Section; Mr D.A. McBrearty, formerly of University of Cambridge; Mr H. Miles, British Astronomical Association, Artificial Satellite Section; Mr M. Rowe, TORRO Tornado Data Collection and Research, and Ball Lightning Divisions; and Dr R. White, Institute for Research in Meteorological Optics. Thanks are also due to those of the UK Voluntary Observing Fleet whose photographs of sea state are included.

Marine Division
Met. Office,
Bracknell, UK.
January 1995.

CHAPTER 1

ATMOSPHERIC PRESSURE

The instrument most commonly used for measuring the pressure of the atmosphere is the precision aneroid barometer. Until recently, the consistent accuracy required for scientific purposes and for official meteorological work could be achieved only by use of the mercury barometer because of certain inherent errors in the aneroid instrument. The marine-type mercury barometer was in regular use aboard British observing ships from 1854 onwards and was so successful that its design remained virtually unchanged through the years.

The precision aneroid is now the standard Met. Office atmospheric pressure reading instrument for issue to voluntary observing ships, as it has proved to be of similar accuracy yet more compact in size and easier to read than the marine mercury barometer, which is subject to 'pumping'. Both instruments are described below.

THE ANEROID BAROMETER

The principle of the aneroid barometer was first suggested in 1698 but no useful instrument was constructed until 1843. The aneroid barometer consists of a circular metallic chamber exhausted of air and hermetically sealed. Variations of atmospheric pressure produce changes in the dimensions of the vacuum chamber and these changes are magnified mechanically, optically or electrically so that the atmospheric pressure may be read on a convenient scale.

The majority of aneroid barometers indicate the pressure by means of a pointer which rotates around a graduated dial. The vacuum chamber, usually called the aneroid capsule, has to provide the force needed to move the pointer and this prevents it from responding freely to pressure variations. This type of instrument is useful in showing pressure changes and some of the better quality instruments are suitable for all pressure readings. The aneroid has the advantage that, unlike the mercurial barometer, it does not suffer from 'pumping', although it does rise and fall slightly with change of height of the ship in the waves of a seaway.

Precision aneroid barometer
The Met. Office standard instrument is the type of precision aneroid barometer (PAB) in which the force required to operate the indicating mechanism is provided by the observer, allowing the capsule to respond freely to pressure changes. The sensing element is a stack of three disc-type aneroid capsules fixed to the inside wall of a cast metal box. Some magnification of the capsule movement is provided by a lever, pivoted on jewelled bearings. One end of the lever is kept in contact with the capsule by means of a light hairspring and a micrometer screw, which extends through the case and actuates a digital counter, which is brought into contact with the other end of the lever by the observer. Contact is indicated by a small cathode-

ray tube; a continuous line of light indicates that contact is made and a broken line of light indicates that the circuit is broken. When the micrometer screw is set so that the contact is just broken the digital counter indicates the pressure in millibars and tenths. The box containing the aneroid capsules is completely airtight except for one hole, and that orifice is fitted with a damping device which restricts the response of the instrument to the rapid pressure variations caused by the rise and fall of the ship.

The Precision Aneroid Barometer Mk. 2 (as shown in Figures 1 and 2) is the type issued to Voluntary Observing Ships.

Installation of the Mk. 2 aneroid barometer. The installation of the barometer on board ship should be carried out by the Port Met. Officer. It should be mounted on a mounting plate, preferably on a fore-and-aft bulkhead. When this has been done the damping cap should be fitted. Firstly unscrew the static vent (Figure 1) reverse it and screw it back in finger-tight, making sure that the O-ring on the static tube beds firmly.

Reading the Mk. 2 aneroid barometer. Press the black switch button. If the thread of light in the cathode ray indicator is broken, turn the knob so that the pressure reading decreases until the thread becomes continuous. When the light is continuous turn the knob so that the pressure reading increases until the thread of light breaks. This should be repeated to avoid any error due to overshooting. At the point where the thread of light breaks, the pressure shown in the window should be read off. If parts of two figures show equally in the tenth-of-a-millibar position the odd number should be taken. In later models of PAB the light thread is replaced by small illuminated red arrows, or triangles, above and below the window, which indicate the direction in which the knob should be turned to obtain a reading, shown by both arrows lighting up alternately.

The pressure as read must be corrected to mean sea level. First apply the correction shown on the calibration correction card supplied and then apply the correction given on the barometer correction card supplied. This must be done for all observations. (See also Table 1 on page 204.)

Maintenance of the Mk. 2 aneroid barometer. The only maintenance required is the renewal of the batteries at approximately twelve-month intervals. When the indicator thread or arrow becomes dim and it is difficult to see whether or not it is broken, the batteries should be changed.

Corrections to aneroid readings

Aneroid barometers of good quality are compensated, by the manufacturers, for such changes in temperature as they are likely to experience, either by leaving a calculated small amount of air in the vacuum chamber, or by use of a bimetallic lever. Such aneroids, therefore, do not require correcting for temperature. Aneroids do not require correcting for latitude, as the principle on which they are based is the balancing of atmospheric pressure by the elasticity of metal, so that the force of gravity does not come into the picture. The only corrections which should be applied to an aneroid reading are those for altitude (see Table 1) and for index error where necessary.

Precautions necessary with an aneroid barometer

The instrument should be placed where it is not liable to sudden jars which may alter its index correction, rapid changes of temperature and where the sun cannot

Figure 1.   Precision Aneroid Barometer Mk. 2 — general view.
Note the housed static vent on left side beneath cap.

Figure 2.   Precision Aneroid Barometer Mk. 2 — interior.

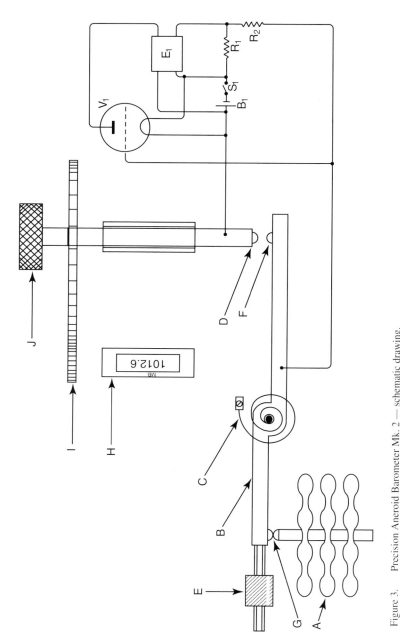

Figure 3. Precision Aneroid Barometer Mk. 2 — schematic drawing.

A — Aneroid capsule assembly, B — Pivoted bar, C — Hairspring D — Micrometer-type spindle and nut, E — Counterbalance F — Sliding electrical contacts, G — Mechanical contacts H — Counter, I — Gearing, J — Knob, V₁ — 'Magic-eye' indicator S₁ — Switch, B₁ — Battery. 1.5 V, E₁ — Voltage converter R₁ and R₂ — Resistances

4

shine directly on to it. Dial aneroids should be tapped gently before a reading is taken as the pointer is liable to stick. This is not necessary with digital precision aneroids.

All aneroids require careful comparisons with barometers whose accuracy can be relied upon, as changes in the elasticity of the metal of which the vacuum chamber is composed may cause appreciable variations in the index correction. Such changes are rare in good quality instruments. Every opportunity should be taken when the vessel is in harbour of making a comparison with a reliable barometer. With a Precision Aneroid Barometer Mk. 2 the damping cap should be removed before making a comparison with a check barometer. Comparisons against a mercury barometer while the ship is at sea are not likely to be satisfactory as the readings of a mercury barometer on a moving ship cannot be considered as reliable for this purpose.

All Port Met. Officers and many harbour and Marine Offices have a standard barometer which is available for such comparisons. A record should be kept of all barometer comparisons made on a ship; this will be useful in assessing the reliability of the instrument and the correction to be applied to dial aneroids when at sea.

Adjustment of aneroid readings
The reading of a dial aneroid may be corrected, if desired, by means of the adjusting screw at the back. Whenever such an alteration of the index correction is made, the fact should be noted, with the date. Such adjustments should, however, only be made if the index correction becomes too great; small changes in the index error of the instrument should be allowed for by altering the correction to the applied readings. No attempt should be made to alter the settings of the Met. Office Precision Aneroid Barometer Mk. 2.

THE MERCURY BAROMETER

The use of mercury barometers for measuring atmospheric pressure has been gradually phased out during recent years, in favour of the precision aneroid barometer. However, some vessels of certain countries participating in the World Meteorological Organization scheme of Voluntary Observing Ships are equipped with mercury barometers, and therefore a general description of their construction and use is included.

The principle of the mercury barometer was discovered by Evangelista Torricelli in 1643.

A simple mercury barometer (Figure 4) is made by completely filling with mercury a glass tube closed at one end and approximately 1 m in length. The open end is then immersed in a cistern also containing mercury, and the tube is held upright. The mercury column falls, leaving a vacuum at the top of the tube, until the weight of the mercury column above the level of the mercury in the cistern just balances the atmospheric pressure which is exerted on the free surface of the mercury in the cistern.

The mercury barometer only gradually passed from this original simple form to that of a practical and portable instrument and was not used by seamen until a century had elapsed.

5

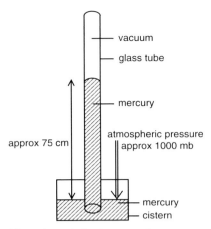

Figure 4.   A simple mercury barometer.

For the purpose of ascertaining the temperature of the barometer itself, a thermometer is attached. On barometers graduated in millibars (hectopascals) the thermometer is graduated in degrees Absolute on older instruments, but in degrees Celsius on those made after 1 January 1955; on inch barometers, it is usually graduated in degrees Fahrenheit.

Graduation of barometer scales
From the invention of the barometer until comparatively recent times the reading was expressed as the height of the mercury column necessary to balance the atmospheric pressure at that instant. In the British Isles, atmospheric pressure was therefore expressed in inches and decimals of an inch, while countries using the metre as a unit of length gave the pressure in millimetres and decimals of a millimetre. The graduations are marked on a metal scale at the side of the instrument. Barometer scales graduated in inches are readable by vernier to a thousandth of an inch (0.001).

Pressure is force per unit area and the measurement of a force is the acceleration it would give to a body of unit mass which is free to move. In the International System of Units (SI)*, now adopted by most countries, the unit of force is the newton (symbol N), the force which, if applied to a mass of 1 kilogram will produce an acceleration of 1 metre per second. The unit of pressure is the pascal (symbol Pa) which is a force of 1 newton per square metre. Use of the millibar as a unit of pressure has been universal in the field of meteorology and is being superseded by the hectopascal, as decreed by the World Meteorological Organization. The millibar continues to be used by the Met. Office as it is familiar to users and will continue to be printed as such in Met. Office marine publications.

1 mb = 1 millibar = 100 pascals = 1 hectopascal = 1 hPa.

In mercury barometers the pressure exerted by the atmosphere is balanced against a column of mercury. Any change in the length of the mercury column is

* Further information on the SI system will be found in Appendix I.

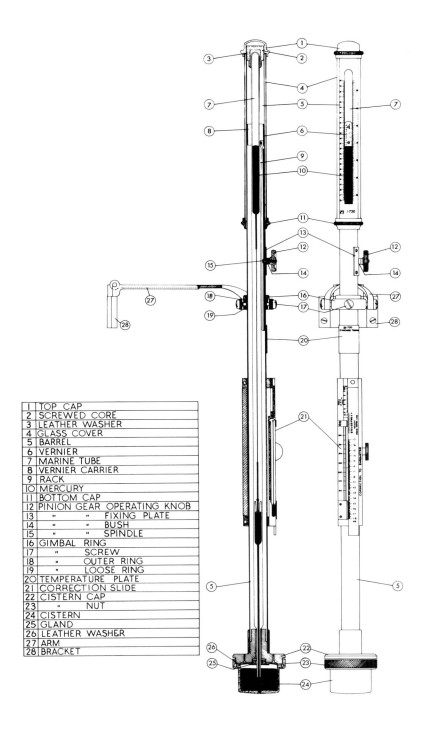

1	TOP CAP
2	SCREWED CORE
3	LEATHER WASHER
4	GLASS COVER
5	BARREL
6	VERNIER
7	MARINE TUBE
8	VERNIER CARRIER
9	RACK
10	MERCURY
11	BOTTOM CAP
12	PINION GEAR OPERATING KNOB
13	" " FIXING PLATE
14	" " BUSH
15	" " SPINDLE
16	GIMBAL RING
17	" SCREW
18	" OUTER RING
19	" LOOSE RING
20	TEMPERATURE PLATE
21	CORRECTION SLIDE
22	CISTERN CAP
23	" NUT
24	CISTERN
25	GLAND
26	LEATHER WASHER
27	ARM
28	BRACKET

Figure 5.   The Kew-pattern marine barometer.

accompanied by a change in the level of the mercury in the cistern. The height of the mercury column depends on atmospheric pressure, density of the mercury and gravity. Standard conditions are laid down under which a barometer should read correctly. These are density of mercury at a temperature of 0 °C, 13 595.1 kilograms per cubic metre (kg/m³), and a conventional datum for gravity of 9.80665 metres per second per second (m/s²).

The Kew-pattern marine barometer
The Kew-pattern marine barometer was the standard issue by the Met. Office prior to the introduction of the precision aneroid barometer. In this type the level of the mercury in the cistern does not have to be adjusted as the scale on the barometer is constructed to allow for changes in the level of the mercury cistern.

The Kew-pattern barometer consists of a glass tube and cistern enclosed in a metal protecting case (Figure 6). In the upper part of the cistern are one or more small holes which admit the air, and a leather washer, permeable to air, which prevents the mercury from escaping, and also keeps out dust. The bore of the glass tube is considerably constricted for the greater part of its length, and, for part of this constriction, is reduced to a fine capillary. The object of these constrictions is to reduce the amount of 'pumping', i.e. oscillations of the top of the mercury column, caused by the movements of the ship and by gusts of wind. At the top of the mercury column the bore of the tube is greater; this minimizes the effect of 'capillarity'* on the height of the centre of the mercury column, but leaves the upper surface of the column sufficiently convex to facilitate accurate reading. An air-trap in the tube prevents air from rising into the space above the mercury column, which should be an almost perfect vacuum. On the metal protecting case is a scale, with a vernier for reading the height of the mercury.

Corrections to mercury barometers
The procedures for preparing corrections for these barometers are no longer dealt with in this handbook. For those interested in determining them, however, reference should be made to the 10th edition of the *Marine Observer's Handbook* (1977, reprinted to 1993), obtainable from the Marine Division, Bracknell.

THE BAROGRAPH

A typical barograph is shown in Figure 7. It is constructed on exactly the same principle as the aneroid barometer, but records its readings by the movement of a pen over a suitable chart.

To increase the movement through which the pen travels in response to pressure changes, the vacuum chamber takes the form of either a number of individual

---

* Capillarity is the tendency of liquids in narrow tubes to rise above or fall below the hydrostatic level. This tendency depends on the relative attraction of the molecules of the liquid for one another and for the molecules of the material of the tube. The narrower the tube, the greater the tendency to rise or fall, so that the effect is particularly well marked in hair-like or capillary tubes, hence the word 'capillarity'. If the liquid wets the solid material, it will rise in a glass tube, but if not, it will be depressed. In the case of water in a glass tube, therefore, the water column is raised, particularly at the edge, while the reverse is the case with mercury in a glass tube, since mercury does not wet glass.

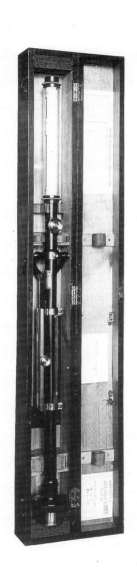
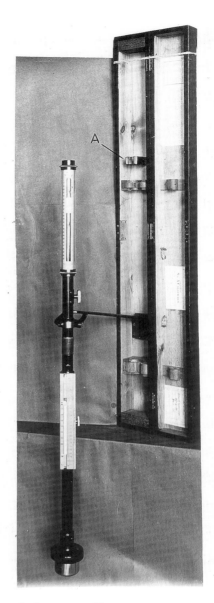

Figure 6.   The Kew-pattern marine barometer and its stowage.

capsules or one large chamber with corrugated walls. The bottom of this vacuum chamber is anchored to the pen arm through a series of levers which still further magnify the movement by pressure changes and which can be arranged to compensate for temperature changes. The variation of volume of the vacuum chamber is thus translated into a vertical movement of the pen arm. This pen arm carries a patented felt stylus or pen and pressure changes are presented as a mark on a chart attached to a clockwork-operated drum. This pressure is recorded as a

9

Figure 7.   The marine open-scale barograph.

continuous line whose height at any point represents the pressure at the time it was recorded. This record is known as a barogram.

The barograph is a valuable adjunct to the barometer aboard ship in providing a continuous record of atmospheric pressure between the times at which the barometer was read. The barograph is not a precision instrument and should never be used as an alternative to the barometer for measuring atmospheric pressure at fixed times. Its advantage is that it provides a graphical record of fluctuations of pressure, together with the times at which they occur, such as the moment of passing of a line squall and its readings are valuable to the meteorologist and to the mariner for various practical purposes.

The open-scale barograph.   Barographs may be made in various scales of size, the smaller being more convenient when space is limited. In such smaller instruments the vacuum chamber and the clock drum are themselves smaller, and the pressure changes recorded on the chart are of a correspondingly reduced scale. To report barometric tendencies with the accuracy required for synoptic meteorological observations, it is desirable that larger, and hence more open-scaled barographs are used. Records from such barographs, when carried on board ships may, however, be unsatisfactory because, due to their greater sensitivity, the trace is not a fine line but a ribbon of appreciable width, resulting from vibration, pressure changes from gusts of wind and from the movement of the ship. Because of this, an oil-damped open-scale barograph (Met. Office Marine Mk. 2) is used on board UK Selected Ships. In this instrument the vacuum chamber is contained in a brass

10

cylinder filled with silicone oil which, to compensate for changes of volume of the vacuum chamber, must pass through a small orifice. In this way short time-period changes are damped out and only the major persistent changes shown on the chart. As a further precaution against vibration the instrument is mounted on rubber pads.

Care of the barograph. The barograph is a delicate instrument and must be handled carefully. Friction between the working parts of the apparatus must be avoided as far as possible. The bearings should be cleaned occasionally and oiled with good clock oil, care being taken to remove excess clock oil.

Friction occurs between the pen and the paper on which it writes. The pressure of the pen on the paper should be reduced to the minimum consistent with a continuous trace; this pressure should be tested from time to time.

In the open-scale barograph the pen arm which carries the pen is suspended like a gate and it is so arranged that the slope of the gate bearings is adjustable. It is thus possible to regulate the pressure of the pen on the chart. In Figure 7, A denotes the gate suspension which is suitably adjusted before issue. The barograph, when used on board ship, should be located in a position where it will be least affected by concussion, vibration or movement of the ship.

Setting of the barograph. The barograph is set to give the correct mean-sea-level reading by comparison with the reading of the precision aneroid barometer after it has been corrected to give mean-sea-level pressure.

In the type of barograph shown in Figure 7, the setting is made by adjusting the height of the fulcrum of the principle lever B by means of the milled head screw C on the central bridge.

Standardizing the barograph. Like the aneroid barometer, and for the same reason (the possibility of changes in the elasticity of the metal of which the vacuum boxes are composed), the readings of the barograph should be compared at least once a week with those of a barometer, duly corrected. The most suitable time is when the weekly chart is changed, and the reading of the barometer, together with the date and UTC, should be entered on the chart.

Adjustments to the barograph should not be made too frequently, but only if its readings become appreciably different from those of the barometer, and a note of the adjustment should be made on the chart, giving date and time. If, after initial installation, the barograph trace appears to be erratic when compared with barometer readings, first check if the brass plug on top of the oil cylinder has been unscrewed and raised on its spindle (see 'Carriage of barograph' below). If this appears to be in order and the barograph is still erratic, the error must be reported to a Port Met. Officer or the responsible Met. Office.

Whenever it appears that the pen may be about to go above or below the barogram in extremes of high or low pressure, the position of the pen arm may be temporarily adjusted, by 10 millibars for instance, as described above and a note made on the chart to this effect. In this way extremes of pressure would be recorded instead of being lost beyond the top or bottom edges of the chart. After passage of the extremes the pen arm should be reset and compared again with the barometer for accuracy of setting.

The barograph clock and chart. The barograph may be fitted with various clocks which will rotate a drum quickly or slowly as desired, round which the chart is fixed. For many applications a rotation in 24 hours will be necessary to show up the small-scale features of pressure changes but, for use at sea, the clock chosen will rotate the drum once per week. The chart must therefore be changed weekly, the clock being wound at the same time. Before removing the chart from a small barograph the pen arm must first be moved away from the chart by means of the lever provided. On open-scale barographs the pen arm automatically lifts off the chart when the lid is lifted. Before the new chart is put on the drum, the date and time should be entered on it. Time marks should be made each day at 1200 UTC and just before the chart is removed, the times being entered on the chart, for the purpose of correcting the time scale should the barograph clock run fast or slow. The barograph should be kept to UTC throughout the voyage. For the purpose of making time marks, barographs have a small button on the outer case which, when depressed, acts on a rubber roller (D in Figure 7) which slightly moves the pen arm vertically.

Before fixing the chart on the drum, the latter must first be lifted from the clock by removing the key and unscrewing the milled nut which holds the drum in place. The chart is then placed round the drum where it is held in position by two short spring clips that hold its top and bottom edges. When fixing the chart on the drum, care must be taken that the horizontal lines printed on the chart are parallel to the flange at the base of the drum. As the length of the chart is slightly greater than the circumference of the drum, there is some overlap when the chart is put on the drum. The last portion of the chart should come on top of the first portion, so that if the chart is not changed at the end of seven days, the pen will not catch on the edge of the chart and tear it, or damage itself.

The drum is then replaced on the clock and the whole is rotated until the pen records the correct UTC. In order to avoid time errors that might be caused by backlash in the teeth of the clock gears, the final movement of the drum, when setting it, should be opposite to the normal direction of rotation.

Carriage of barograph. Before removing the barograph from its position on board ship, the brass plug on top of the oil cylinder (E in Figure 7) should be pushed down its spindle and screwed in place tightly to prevent leakage of the silicone damping oil in transit. Oil leakage will seriously damage the barograph mechanism. The pen arm should be attached to the pen lifter. The reverse procedure applies when a barograph is installed.

THE CHANGE OR TENDENCY OF THE BAROMETER

The change or tendency of the barometer, always a valuable observation to seamen, is also of considerable value to the forecaster.

The barometric tendency, by international usage, is defined as the change in the barometric pressure in the last three hours. It is required in radio weather messages and is read off from the barograph. The position of the pen on the chart at the time of observation, and the reading of the trace three hours earlier, should be noted, if possible to the tenth of a millibar. The difference between these two readings will give the tendency. It should not be taken as the difference between two readings on the barometer, but should always be read off from the barograph, since the barograph method is less liable to error, and anyway the barometer is not customarily read every three hours at sea. Also, mistakes in reading a barograph are more likely to be detected, owing to the continuous availability of the trace.

It is essential that the barograph trace should be fine and sensitive, with the instrument free from mechanical faults such as sticking, and as far as possible not vitiated by the effects of vibration, or of unequal heating due to sunshine or nearby sources of heat.

Allowance for course and speed
To estimate the true tendency of the barometer reported from a ship under way, a meteorological service needs to allow for course and speed, and, therefore, in a ship's weather report provision is made for reporting the course and speed of the ship. The allowance for the course and speed of the ship should not be made by the observer on board ship when reporting tendency in a weather message. This allowance can be readily made at the meteorological office ashore when the observations are studied by forecasters or processed by computers.

The characteristic of the barometric tendency
This is the name given to the coded description of the nature of the changes the pressure has undergone in the last three hours. It is required in ships' weather reports, and is read off from the barograph trace. The diagrams in Figure 8 show the various pressure changes that might have to be reported, together with the code figures to be used in reporting them.

The codes to be used in reporting the barometric tendency and characteristic are given, with other codes, in the *Ships' Code and Decode Book* (Met.O.509) and in the *Admiralty List of Radio Signals*, Volume 3.

Code Figure	Trace	Description of Curve	Pressure *now*, compared with 3 hours ago
0		Rising, then falling	The same
		Rising, then falling	Higher
1		Rising, then steady	Higher
		Rising, then rising more slowly	
2		Rising, (steadily or unsteadily)	Higher
3		Falling, then rising	Higher
		Steady, then rising	
		Rising, then rising more quickly	
4	—	Steady	The same
5		Falling, then rising	The same
		Falling, then rising	Lower
6		Falling, then steady	Lower
		Falling, then falling more slowly	
7		Falling (steadily or unsteadily)	Lower
8		Steady, then falling	Lower
		Rising, then falling	
		Falling, then falling more quickly	

Figure 8.   Code used to indicate the characteristic of barometric tendency.

The diurnal variation in the pressure

Superposed upon its irregular variations due to changes in the weather, the barometric pressure has a regular rise and fall twice a day, the maximum values occurring at about 10 and 22 hours and the minimum values at about 04 and 16 hours, local time. In temperate regions the amplitude of these diurnal variations is comparatively small, so that they are usually lost in the much greater irregular variations of these regions, but nearer the tropics, the amplitude of the diurnal variation increases and the magnitude of other changes in general decreases, so that the diurnal variations become very marked and can be clearly seen, day after day, on a barograph chart. In these regions, therefore, barometric changes do not indicate changes in the weather, unless they remain considerable after the diurnal variation has been discounted.

Tables have been prepared for the Atlantic, Pacific and Indian Oceans, between latitudes 0° and 20°, N or S, showing the corrections for diurnal variation to be applied to the observed pressure to reduce it to the mean for the day, and the average values of the barometric change in an hour, throughout the day, due to the diurnal variation. These tables are given in the meteorological text of the appropriate Admiralty Sailing Directions. Corresponding figures do not differ greatly from one ocean to another or between north and south latitudes and have been averaged in this handbook to give values that will be approximately correct in any ocean for the two bands of latitude 0–10°, N or S, and 10–20°, N or S. These values are shown in Tables 2 and 3, also Figure 9. In the tropics, should the barometer, after correction for diurnal variation (Table 2), be as much as 3 millibars below the monthly normal for the locality, the mariner should be on the alert, as there is a distinct possibility that a tropical cyclone has formed, or is forming. A comparison of subsequent hourly changes in his barometer with the corresponding figures in Table 3 will show whether these changes indicate a real further fall in pressure and, if so, its amount.

When the observer on board ship is reporting barometric tendency, or entering it up in his log, he should not correct it for changes due to normal diurnal variation. This correction, like the correction for course and speed of the ship, is made, if necessary, as a matter of routine by the meteorological office receiving the observations.

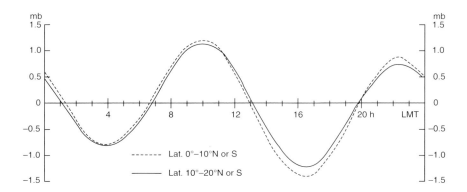

Figure 9. Mean diurnal variation of pressure.

CHAPTER 2

THE MEASUREMENT OF TEMPERATURE AND HUMIDITY

The temperatures normally measured at sea for meteorology are those of the air, at the height of the bridge, and of the sea, just below its surface. Humidity, i.e. a measure of the evaporated water contained in the air, is also required, but as this is obtained by similar instrumentation, it is included under the same general heading.

Thermometers
Any device which measures temperature is a thermometer. There is a wide range of physical phenomena related to temperature, almost any one of which may be used as a thermometer but the two which will be most frequently encountered are based on the expansion of a suitable substance with increased temperature and, similarly, the change of electrical resistance in a conductor. The simplest, cheapest and most commonly encountered device is the liquid-in-glass thermometer, the liquid employed being mercury or alcohol. Such a thermometer consists of a glass tube of very fine bore, at the end of which a bulb has been blown to act as a reservoir. The whole of the tube and bulb is filled with the chosen liquid at a high temperature and the open end of the tube is then sealed. On cooling, the liquid will contract until the tube is only partly filled by liquid, the exact point reached by the liquid being a measure of the temperature of the thermometer, and hence, under suitable conditions, of its surroundings, at any given moment. A scale may now be engraved on the tube, or thermometer stem, to allow actual temperature to be read.

The thermometer was invented at approximately the same time as the barometer. Galileo made a crude kind of thermometer in which the liquid was open to the air. True thermometers were first brought into general use by the Grand Duke Ferdinand II of Tuscany who is said to have possessed such instruments in 1654. The liquid used in these early thermometers was alcohol.

While mercury is the most satisfactory liquid for general thermometric use, thermometers intended for very cold climates contain pure alcohol. The reason for this is that mercury would solidify at the low temperatures of polar regions. Mercury freezes at about −39 °C while alcohol freezes only at −130 °C, though it becomes a thick liquid and therefore useless for thermometric purposes at −90 °C.

Thermometers employing the electrical change of resistance due to temperature give no direct visual indication but must be placed in an electrical circuit which will enable the resistance and hence, from previous calibration, the temperature, to be measured. Such thermometers usually are constructed from a length of fine wire, drawn from a material such as platinum, tungsten, etc., which is ductile and will not corrode with time. For meteorological use, a spool of such wire is permanently enclosed in a small-diameter metal cylinder, for protection.

Graduation of thermometers. The earliest known graduation of a thermometer was that made in 1701 by Sir Isaac Newton, who divided the range of temperature between the freezing point of water and the temperature of the human body into twelve degrees.

Later scientists used as fixed points the temperature of a mixture of salt and ice, and the boiling point (at standard pressure) of water. The SI unit of temperature is the kelvin (symbol K), widely used in scientific work. It is defined as the fraction 1/273.16 of the thermodynamic temperature of the triple point of water; the triple point of a substance being the pressure–temperature condition, unique for a given substance, at which the substance may exist in the solid, liquid or gaseous state. On this scale water freezes at 273.15 K and boils (at standard pressure) at 373.15 K. For normal use the Celsius (known as the centigrade) temperature (symbol °C) has also been approved by the International Committee on Weights and Measures. It is defined as:

$$t = T - T_0$$

where t = Celsius temperature, T = thermodynamic temperature in kelvins, and T_0 = 273.15 K. On this scale water freezes at 0 °C and boils (at standard pressure) at 100 °C. It is the official scale for the measurement of all meteorological temperatures.

The Fahrenheit scale (symbol °F), once in general use in the English-speaking world, now rapidly becoming obsolete, has two fixed points; zero is taken as the temperature of a mixture of salt and ice and 100 as the temperature of the human body. This gives the freezing point of water as 32 °F and the boiling point (at standard pressure) as 212 °F. For a time the Met. Office used a scale of temperature called 'Absolute' which approximated to the scale now called the kelvin. The symbol was °A. On this scale the water froze at 273 °A and boiled (at standard pressure) at 373 °A. This scale may still be found on older mercury barometers and in some correction tables.

Conversion of thermometer scales. To convert Celsius readings to Fahrenheit use the following rule: Multiply by 9/5 and add 32. Similarly, to convert from Fahrenheit to Celsius, subtract 32 and multiply by 5/9. From Fahrenheit to kelvin (formerly known as Absolute), proceed as for Celsius and add 273.15. Table 7 gives the values on the Celsius and kelvin scales corresponding to each degree Fahrenheit, from 0 °F to 119 °F.

Scale markings. Thermometer scales can take various forms. As the liquid-in-glass thermometer is particularly fragile, it is usually protected in some way or other, and the scale is often incorporated in this protection. In the standard Met. Office sheathed thermometer (Figure 10) the scale is engraved directly upon the thermometer stem, the back being coloured to allow easy reading. The thermometer stem is then enclosed in an outer glass tube, which adds to the strength of the whole and protects the scale from erosion. In this case the thermometer is therefore read through the outer glass tube.

Electrical thermometers are usually read by dial and pointer, the pointer either being operated by the resistance thermometer electrical circuits or by manually setting to achieve a prescribed effect — the 'zeroing' of a secondary pointer, or by the lighting or extinction of electric lamps.

Reading the thermometer. The thermometer should be read with care. Ships' thermometers are graduated in half degrees Celsius and the readings should be given by estimation to the nearest tenth of a degree. This is not only necessary for general accuracy but also for practical reasons, i.e. the computation of relative humidity and the dew-point (see page 20), and the determination of the difference

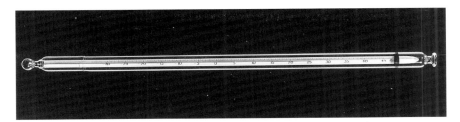

Figure 10.   Air thermometer.

between air and sea-surface temperatures. In some coded radio weather messages, however, the temperature is required only to the nearest degree.

When reading a thermometer, care should be taken to keep the eye at the same level as the end of the column, otherwise there will be an error due to parallax.

The mercury column of a thermometer occasionally separates in one or more places. The thermometers should therefore be examined before each observation to see if the column is continuous. If there is any break in the column, take the instrument down, swing it briskly at arm's length with the bulb end away from you until the column is again continuous, and replace it. After this, give the thermometers another 10 minutes to pick up the correct temperatures again, before taking the observation. With the alcohol-in-glass thermometer some alcohol may flow into the upper end of the tube unless the thermometer is stored with the bulb end downwards.

Thermometers should be kept clean. In damp weather any moisture should be removed from the dry-bulb a little while before taking the reading. The graduations on the glass of mounted thermometers may in time become indistinct. Since the marks are cut in the glass, a rub with an ordinary lead pencil or wipe over with Indian ink will make the graduations clear again.

For all types of liquid-in-glass thermometer it is best always to store in a vertical or near vertical position and never with the bulb higher than the end of the stem. In consequence a spare thermometer is most conveniently retained in its box, which can be conveniently located in a rack or a clip which will hold it in a vertical position.

THE DRY- AND WET-BULB THERMOMETERS

An instrument for measuring the humidity of the air is called a hygrometer. There are several kinds of hygrometers, but the form in common use, the dry- and wet-bulb thermometers, also known as Mason's hygrometer or a psychrometer, is the simplest and is described below.

Of the two thermometers contained in the thermometer screen, no more need be said of the dry-bulb for measuring air temperature, beyond ensuring that it is secured firmly into the clips provided. The operation of and attention to the wet-bulb thermometer requires a little further description.

Operation of a wet-bulb thermometer. The evaporation of water requires heat, the 'latent heat of evaporation'. This is derived from the surroundings — the air, the water itself and/or from the thermometer used for the measurement. The faster the evaporation the greater the demand for latent heat and hence the greater will be the cooling of the surroundings. However, the rate of evaporation under any particular circumstance will be determined by the dryness of the surrounding air, the air temperature and the rate at which air flows past the thermometer. A measure of humidity, i.e. the degree of dryness or wetness of the air, can thus be obtained by wetting a thermometer and noting the degree to which it is cooled. In practice it is both inconvenient and unnecessary to wet the whole thermometer — wetting the bulb alone will suffice. The bulb itself is thus enclosed in a small muslin bag, tied on by means of a wick, the other end of which is placed in a small water container placed beside the thermometer. Capillary action will then ensure that the muslin is kept wet, and the cooling action of evaporation can then be measured by reading, firstly, the dry-bulb thermometer, then the wet-bulb thermometer and by subtraction, the difference, the 'wet-bulb depression'. The third requirement is knowledge of the rate of the air flow. A value has been assumed so that, from the air temperature and wet-bulb depression, a reasonably correct measure of humidity may be obtained from the tables provided. This combination of a dry- and wet-bulb thermometer is known as a psychrometer.

Air can contain only a limited amount of evaporated water, according to its temperature. When this point is reached, no further evaporation will take place and the wet-bulb thermometer will read the same as the dry-bulb thermometer. The air is then said to be saturated. If the air becomes drier, the rate of evaporation increases and the wet-bulb temperature falls. The depression of the wet-bulb can reach over 20 °C in a hot dry climate, such as that of Khartoum during part of the year. It sometimes amounts to 10 °C in England, but at sea the difference seldom reaches 5 °C. When the humidity of the atmosphere is high, during or just before or after rain, when fog is prevalent, or when dew is forming, there is little or no evaporation and the two thermometers give the same, or very nearly the same reading.

We may sum up the facts about humidity and the dry- and wet-bulb thermometers as under:

Humidity	Evaporation	
High ...	Weak ...	Dry- and wet-bulbs read almost the same.
Low ...	Intense ...	Wet-bulb reads much lower than dry.

Muslin and wick for wet-bulbs. The wet-bulb thermometer needs careful attention in order to get correct readings. The bulb of this thermometer should be covered with a single thickness of thin clean muslin or cambric, which is kept moist by attaching to it a few threads of darning cotton dipping into the small reservoir of water placed near it.

From the muslin provided, a small piece should be cut, sufficient to cover the bulb, and should be stretched smoothly over it, creases being avoided as far as possible. The muslin is kept in place by attaching the cotton wick in the following way. Take a round turn in the wick, with the strands middled on the bight, and pass the ends through the bight, forming a round turn and cow hitch. Any superfluous muslin or loose ends should then be trimmed off (Figure 11a).

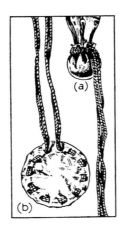

Figure 11.   (a) Wet-bulb with ordinary muslin and wick. (b) Muslin cap.

Muslin caps ready threaded with cotton are usually supplied. These are slipped over the bulb, and the thread is then pulled tight and tied (Figure 11b). The strands should be long enough to reach two or three inches below the lowest part of the bulb, in order that their lower ends can be immersed in the water vessel, but not long enough to hang in a bight, or water will drip from the wick at the lowest point of the curve until the reservoir is emptied.

Precautions necessary in taking wet-bulb observations.   To get correct readings the muslin must be damp, but not dripping. If it is too wet, the reading of the thermometer will be too high. If it is not wet enough, the reading will again be too high. The former defect may be cured by cutting down the number of threads supplying moisture to the bulb. Take care, however, that this remedy does not make the muslin too dry.

It is important that the water should be pure. Ordinary water contains substances in solution and, if such water is used, as it evaporates it deposits these substances on the thread and muslin; the free flow of water to the muslin and its evaporation therefrom are checked, and the thermometer may read too high. Moreover, the rate of evaporation from impure water may differ appreciably from that for pure water. It is therefore desirable that distilled water should be used. This may be available from the ship's radio office, but is liable to become contaminated with acid in the course of a voyage. If, therefore, sufficient distilled water can be collected from the ship's radio office at the commencement of a voyage, this should be used. If distilled water is not available, condenser water from the engine-room may be used. Fresh water should only be used as a last resort.

The muslin should be changed at least once a week and more often if it becomes dirty or contaminated by salt spray. The presence of salt in the water will cause the thermometer to read too high and, if any spray has reached the instrument, the muslin and wick should be replaced by new ones. It is advisable to do this in any case after bad weather. If it is found that an encrustation of lime or other impurity has formed on the thermometer bulb, this should be scraped off. A note should be made in the appropriate column of the meteorological logbook whenever the muslin is changed.

After the muslin has been changed, some time must be allowed to elapse before observations are resumed. This is to ensure that the proper degree of wetting has been achieved and that the thermometer and wetted muslin have attained the properly balanced temperature.

Wet-bulb temperature higher than dry-bulb. If the reading of the wet-bulb thermometer is above that of the dry-bulb, first make sure that the readings were correct. Then ensure that the muslin and thread are moist but not too wet and that the dry-bulb is indeed dry. (If the latter has to be wiped, allow it to cool to the air temperature before a second reading.) If no fault is found, book the temperatures as they have been read and note in the 'Remarks' column that the reading has been checked, the muslin and thread examined, and that the ventilation is adequate.

Except as a result of a defect, it is impossible in normal circumstances for the wet-bulb to read higher than the dry if a temperature is steady, and if the wet-bulb is above freezing point (see below). If the temperature is changing, however, one of the thermometers may be more sensitive than the other and follow the temperature changes with less lag. Under such circumstances it is possible that the wet-bulb thermometer may sometimes be found to be reading higher than the dry-bulb. In such a case the wet-bulb should be taken as correct and the dry-bulb reading adjusted to equality with the wet-bulb. If this phenomenon occurs frequently and the fault cannot otherwise be traced, it may lie in one of the thermometers. These should be examined and if there is nothing obviously wrong the spare thermometer should be brought into use to replace the first one, and then (if necessary) the other thermometer, till satisfactory observations are again obtained.

Wet-bulb readings during frost. During frost, when the muslin is thinly coated with ice, the readings are still valid because evaporation takes place from a surface of ice as freely as from one of water. If the muslin is dry it must be given an ice coating by wetting it slightly with ice-cold water, using a camel-hair brush or by other means. The water will usually take 10 to 15 minutes to freeze. Excess of water must not be used as it takes much longer to freeze and will also not give accurate readings. After the wetting of the muslin, the temperature generally remains steady at 0 °C until all the water has been converted to ice. It then begins to fall gradually to the true ice-bulb reading. No reading must be recorded until the temperature of the ice-bulb has fallen below that of the dry-bulb and remains steady. Dry, windy weather may cause the ice to evaporate completely before the time of the next reading, in which case the procedure of wetting the bulb must be gone through again. The original coating of ice will give satisfactory results as long as it lasts.

It must be pointed out that supercooled water may exist on the wet-bulb at temperatures well below freezing point and that, if this is not noticed by the observer, serious errors will occur. The freezing can be started by touching the wet-bulb with a snow crystal, a pencil, or other object.

Measures of humidity. Dew-point and relative humidity can be obtained from the readings of the dry- and wet-bulb.

The dew-point is the temperature at which dew would begin to form on the bulb of the thermometer if the air were cooled down, the amount of water vapour in it remaining unchanged. Tables 4 and 5 give the dew-point for dry-bulb temperatures and depressions of the wet-bulb. The depression of the wet bulb is the difference between the dry- and wet-bulb readings. The amount of this depression depends on the ventilation to which the wet-bulb thermometer is subjected and Table 4 is to be used for observations in which the thermometers are exposed in the standard marine screen. Since the amount of evaporation from ice and water surfaces is not the same, lines are ruled in the tables to call attention to the fact that above the line evaporation is going on from a water surface while below the line it is going on from an ice surface. Intermediate figures must therefore be obtained by extrapolation.

In order that values of the wet-bulb depression of the necessary accuracy shall be available, it is especially desirable at low temperatures that the thermometers should be read to the tenth of a degree. This is because at low temperatures dew-point changes rapidly with changes in wet-bulb depression.

The relative humidity is the amount of water vapour actually present in the air, expressed as a percentage of the amount the air would contain at that temperature if it were saturated. Table 6 gives the relative humidity for dry-bulb temperature and depression of the wet-bulb. In the UK Met. Office a relative humidity of 95 per cent is taken as a guide in determining whether to report mist or haze (see tables on page 52).

ELECTRICAL RESISTANCE THERMOMETERS

The electrical resistance of platinum wire varies in a known way with change of temperature. This characteristic is used in electrical resistance thermometers. Thin platinum wire in the form of a helix is enclosed inside a highly conductive ceramic former which is further enclosed in a close-fitting stainless-steel tubular sheath for protection. A plug of epoxy resin is placed in the head of the thermometer to prevent ingress of moisture to the platinum element. Electrical leads are brought

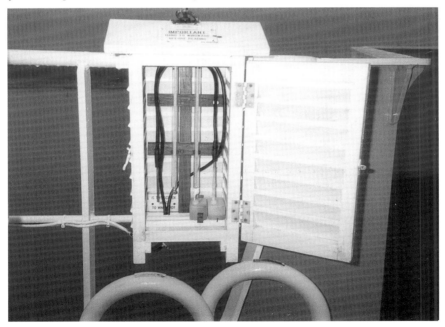

Figure 12.   Marine screen with Electrical Resistance Thermometers.

21

through the head of the thermometer for connection to a suitable device to measure the change in resistance.

The Met. Office Resistance Thermometer Element Mk. 4A has a diameter of 4 mm and stem length of approximately 80 mm and a sensing length of 10 mm at the lower end of the stem. The thermometer is of the four-lead type.

When used as a wet-bulb thermometer a special tight-fitting tubular wick is fitted. Although the sensing part of the thermometer is located in the lower part, the wick should be placed 40 mm up the stem to ensure accurate wet-bulb reading. Sufficient loose wick should be left below the bottom of the thermometer to reach to the bottom of the water bottle. The thermometers are generally used connected to the Met. Office Digital Temperature Indicator Mk. 1B or Mk. 2 (Ships) (Figure 13).

Figure 13.   Digital Temperature Indicators. Top Mk. 1B, bottom Mk. 2.

22

Digital Temperature Indicator (DTI)

The indicator is an integrated digital voltmeter, scaled in temperature, used to indicate temperature sensed by electrical resistance thermometers, which can be set up at some distance. The DTI can be used to read up to eight resistance thermometer elements. On board ship the first five push-button positions are connected to read air temperature, wet-bulb temperature from either port or starboard screens, and sea temperature from the hull sensor. When the instrument has been installed by technical staff, the operator need only press the appropriate push-button on the indicator. The display will stabilize within two seconds of selecting a channel, when the temperature will be displayed as three digits; tens, units and tenths of degrees Celsius. A negative temperature is indicated by a minus sign before the tens digit.

The DTI should always remain switched on. If the power has been switched off the instrument requires 30 minutes to warm up. A display blanking switch is situated on the left-hand side of the indicator. The equipment should be inspected by a Port Met. Officer or technician at approximately six-monthly intervals.

THE MARINE SCREEN

Exposure of thermometers. No matter how accurate a thermometer may be, it can do no more than indicate its own temperature. It is therefore essential that the thermometer is in correct contact with the medium whose temperature it is to measure, in order that it may 'share' its true temperature, and that it is protected from any extraneous source of heat. When measuring the air temperature, particular problems arise on this score, in that the thermometer must be shielded from the heat radiated by the sun, the sea and from the ship itself, yet at the same time the air, which is itself transparent to such radiated heat, must be allowed to flow freely past the thermometer. Even when not in use no normal meteorological thermometer, for whatever purpose it is supplied, must ever be exposed to full sunlight for more than a moment or two, and when stored, should be kept in its packaging.

A thermometer screen is used to shield the thermometer from external radiation, yet allowing an adequate flow of air.

Design of thermometer screen. There are several acceptable designs of thermometer screens, although only one is regarded as the Met. Office standard marine type. The essential features of any such screen, which at present is made of wood, are that the vertical walls are composed of louvres or 'jalousies', constructed so that no direct radiation can reach the thermometers but allowing relatively free air flow to reach the thermometer, while in addition vertical ventilation is permitted through the slotted floor and through holes in an inner roof. Hence, should the air within the screen become warmer or colder than its surroundings, it may rise or sink, and be replaced by outside air of the correct temperature. Such screens are painted white as a further precaution against radiation. Screens should be repainted when necessary and a watch should be kept for possible rotting of the woodwork, particularly in the lower corners. Marine screens contain two thermometers, the dry-bulb and the wet-bulb.

Position of marine screen. The screen should be placed in the open air and, for convenience in reading the thermometers, about 1.5 metres above the deck. It may be exposed in sun or shade, attached to bridge wing rails, so as to have an

Figure 14.   Marine Screen.

unimpeded circulation of air flowing through it. It should be out of the way of unauthorized persons; it must not be exposed to suddenly varying conditions due to causes within the ship, such as draughts of air from boilers, engine-room, etc. The lighting at night should be so arranged that it cannot affect the temperature of the thermometers. By day or by night the light should come from behind or from the side of the observer.

The position of the thermometer screen requires great attention. It cannot be too strongly emphasized that the temperature of the free air is required, not of that affected by heat from the ship. The most suitable location is where the air will come direct on to the screen from the sea before passing over any part of the ship. The ship is a source of local heat; radiation takes place from the hull and from sunny decks, deck houses, etc., especially in the tropics. Radiation of heat, or warm draughts of air, may be felt from galleys, engine and boiler rooms, and funnel. The thermometer screen should be as far as possible removed from all such sources of local heating which will tend to cause false air temperatures, particularly on days when the relative wind is light. The choice of the bridge will avoid some of these sources of heating.

Setting up the thermometers. Sheathed thermometers are held in place by means of three clips. The thermometers should not be allowed to touch the floor of the

24

screen but if they slip down through the clips a rubber grommet (obtainable from Port Met. Officers) should be placed over the thermometer, resting above the top or bottom clip. The plastic water bottle is held in place with a metal clip.

ASPIRATED AND WHIRLING PSYCHROMETERS

The system of measuring humidity by means of dry- and wet-bulb thermometers contained in a louvred thermometer screen assumes that the design of the screen controls the internal air flow between limits usually taken as 2–4 knots. Although in the open air the assumption appears reasonably correct, there will be occasions when greater accuracy is needed or, for temporary observations, a thermometer screen cannot be erected. Moreover, the assumption will rarely, if ever, be true if temperatures and humidities are to be measured in confined spaces, for example within the hold of a ship.

The difficulty is overcome by artificially ventilating the thermometers at a controlled rate. Such thermometers are said to be 'aspirated'. Aspiration is performed by a fan which, operated by electric or clockwork motor, or even by hand (at a controlled speed) will draw air over the thermometers at a known rate. Aspirated thermometer systems include their own shield against direct radiation. An even more simple system ensures adequate ventilation by whirling or rotating the thermometers by hand at a controlled rate, the thermometers being mounted in a suitable holder to permit this. Such hand-held psychrometers are normally provided with no precautions against radiation whatsoever and must therefore be used only in the shade. This is also desirable in the case of the mechanically aspirated psychrometer.

As the rate of ventilation produced by aspirated and whirled psychrometers differs from that assumed to prevail in the static thermometer screen, different hygrometric tables must be employed, and the greatest care must be taken to ensure that the tables appropriate to the method are in fact used. Table 5, at the end of this book, is the one to be employed with aspirated and whirling psychrometers. As with Table 4, lines are ruled to draw attention to the fact that above the line evaporation is taking place from a water surface, while below the line it is occurring from an ice surface. Interpolation of readings must therefore not be made between figures on different sides of the line.

THE APPLICATION OF HYGROMETRIC OBSERVATIONS IN THE CARE AND PROPER VENTILATION OF CARGO

Sweating, or the deposition of moisture, is a frequent cause of damage, both to cargo and to the internal structure of a ship, and it is desirable to keep a record, not only of the temperature and humidity of the outside air through which the ship is passing, but also of the temperature and humidity of the air in each hold, as far as this is practicable. Although deductions from such data will vary according to the nature of the cargo and the construction of the ship, experience of these observations should help the seaman to judge whether, at any particular time, his cargo and the structure of his ship are in danger of damage by moisture and whether conditions are likely to be improved, or the reverse, by ventilation.

SEA TEMPERATURE

The routine meteorological requirement is for observation of sea-water temperature taken from near or just below the surface. The precise depth is not specified but any one of several methods is regarded as adequate. These methods are:

(a)   by obtaining a sample by bucket;
(b   by thermometer immersed in the sea or in proximity to the sea;
(c)   by engine-room intake temperature;
(d)   by Met. Office supplied electronic distant reading equipment with hull-mounted sea sensor;
(e)   by Expendable Bathythermograph (XBT).

Bucket method
From a slow-moving ship having a bridge height of up to about 10 metres it is comparatively easy to draw a sample of sea water on board by almost any form of bucket strong enough to withstand the water pressure while being towed. A thermometer may then be inserted and the water temperature measured. Small buckets made of double-skinned canvas or rubber are very suitable for this purpose. Single-skinned canvas buckets are not suitable because any evaporation from the sides of the bucket would lower the temperature of the water sample.

The problem of obtaining a sea-water sample with a bucket becomes increasingly difficult as ships' size, speed and height of bridge are increased. Canvas buckets are so light that they would obviously be unsuitable for a fast ship from a high bridge. Even if not torn away on entry into the sea, little water would remain by the time it had been drawn up to deck level and the bucket's life would be very short. A smaller and somewhat heavier bucket made of rubber reinforced by canvas is now supplied to all UK Voluntary Observing Ships. This bucket is little more than a closed length of rubber hose and it is suitable for taking sea temperatures in almost any ship, but a complete solution of successfully using a bucket regardless of the size and speed of ship has yet to be found. Extensive trials with this rubber bucket have shown that the temperature of the water sample changes very slowly after it has been hove on deck.

The small rubber buckets described above were originally designed to contain a thermometer which was lowered and immersed in the sea with the bucket itself. A high rate of thermometer breakage was experienced and the policy now is to immerse the thermometer in its sheath into the sample of sea water when the bucket is drawn up on deck. There is in fact little disadvantage in this: whether the thermometer is immersed in the sea or inserted later, it will do no more than measure the temperature of the sample at the moment of observing.

Whichever type of bucket is used, it should be swung as far out as possible to avoid the shallow layers of water close to the hull which have been warmed by the ship itself. Probably the best way of getting the water sample is to use the bucket as though one were taking a cast of the hand lead. On entering the water the bucket should submerge quickly and cleanly. If drawn along the surface, a fault to which some designs are particularly prone, it will be filled with spray, possessing some temperature intermediate to that of the sea and that of the air.

Figure 15.   Sea temperature bucket and thermometer.

On being withdrawn, a thermometer should be inserted into the sample immediately. This should be done in the shade; direct sunlight, in addition to its direct effect upon the thermometer, can warm the sea-water sample very quickly.

Individual thermometers are calibrated either for complete immersion into the medium whose temperature is to be measured, or for contact through the thermometer bulb alone (e.g. clinical thermometers). Meteorological thermometers are invariably of the former class and, if not large, would give rise to unacceptable errors when the air/sea temperature differences are large. In consequence the whole thermometer should be covered by the sea water without touching either the sides or bottom of the bucket. Devices which hold the thermometer within the bucket may be available, but otherwise it should be held at the extreme end by finger tip, without actually letting the fingers (which are a source of heat) enter the sample.

27

With the large canvas bucket the thermometer should be moved with a slow stirring action. After immersion for about one minute the thermometer should be withdrawn just sufficiently to allow the scale to be read, the bulb and as much of the stem as possible being left immersed.

The special sea-temperature thermometer, when supplied, should be used for this purpose, but almost any meteorological thermometer may be used, including those employed for wet- and dry-bulb observations.

After use, the thermometer should be dried and returned to its box for storage with the bulb end downwards.

Distant-reading thermometers

There would obviously be many advantages in measuring temperature by means of a distant-reading instrument while the thermometer bulb was actually immersed in the sea. In its most simple form such a device would be lowered by cable alongside the ship and readings taken inboard while it was towed. There are, however, certain difficulties in such a method. It is difficult to control the depth of such a device or even ensure that it enters the water at all and does not merely skip along the surface. The strain of towing upon the cable can also be a cause of error in the electrical measurements, while a freely towed device could damage itself against the side of the ship.

The system evolved by the Met. Office and installed in new buildings and modern ships places the thermometer inside the hull, measuring the sea temperature by conduction through the ship's side plating, the principle being that steel is such a good conductor that it transmits the temperature of the surrounding sea water. The

Figure 16. Distant-reading sea temperature thermometer plate.

thermometer, which is in the form of a small, thin, printed electrical resistance circuit little bigger than a postage stamp, is fixed to the inside of the hull of the ship at a point a metre or so below the normal water-line. The system which requires the whole plate to change temperature with that of the sea, has a long time lag, and is thus unaffected by short-period roll or pitch, but would be invalidated if the position of the thermometer were raised above sea level by change in loading. The system demands cabling to the place where temperatures are to be read, normally the bridge, and installation is best carried out during the construction of the ship.

Engine-room intake temperatures
The temperature of the engine-room intake water can be taken as a measure of sea-water temperature either by thermometer or by thermograph. To an extent dependent on the individual ship, the accuracy will be questionable although the method is very convenient and may well be the only one possible (in the absence of the hull thermometer described above) when the bucket method cannot be used because of rough seas, too great a ship speed or a bridge too high above the water. The errors arise from the varying depth from which the water is drawn as the ship rolls or pitches and the risk of pre-heating as the water passes through pipes at or close to engine-room temperature or through oil and water tanks on the inside of the hull. A sample of the intake water may be drawn off by tap, the subsequent procedure being that described in the bucket method above, or the temperature measured by a thermometer installed within the intake pipe. In the latter case the thermometer will usually be inserted in a pocket formed within the pipe, and the main problem which then arises is of assuring good thermal conductivity. Digital readings of sea temperature in the engine control room can be relayed by telephone or electronic means to the bridge.

BATHYTHERMOGRAPH

This is an instrument used on board ship for obtaining a sea temperature profile from the surface down to a predetermined depth. Mechanical models consist of a bronze torpedo-shaped instrument which is lowered and recovered by means of a winch, length of wire veered being dependent on ship's speed. The record is etched onto a smoked glass slide by a stylus attached to a bimetallic temperature sensor.

After recovery the slide is removed from the instrument, marked with sounding details, placed in a holder against a graduated scale and read off: discontinuities and turning points are then added before the slide is lacquered to preserve the trace.

EXPENDABLE BATHYTHERMOGRAPH

As the name implies this uses a non-recoverable probe. The equipment used can be considered in three sections:

Expendable Probe.   This section is about 5 cm in diameter and 35 cm in length. It consists of a plastic protective cap, a probe in the shape of a small mortar bomb, a retaining pin and a plastic tube with a reel and protected contacts. Connecting the reel in the tube to a reel in the probe is a length of fine three-core copper wire which is veered when the probe is released, the twin reel system producing a steady rate of descent. On removing the retaining pin at the time of launching, a resistance thermometer housed in the hollow nose of the probe continuously transmits temperature readings via the copper wire.

Launcher and Attached Cable.   A free-running cable enables the launcher to be positioned at various locations near the ship's side, where a successful sounding can be made. This cable connects the launcher to a junction box from which a fixed cable runs to the recorder. The launcher is a gun-like device with pistol grip, into the breech of which the probe is loaded; a cocking mechanism forces contacts into the end of the probe tube.

Recorders.   The recording instruments consist of a chart recorder to register temperature against depth, a metal stylus which etches a trace on waxed paper and a cassette recorder which records the same information on magnetic tape. A manuscript log is also kept from which the completed XBT message is compiled for relay ashore by terrestrial or satellite communication.

A completed series of soundings identifies the movement of subsurface currents, the onset of thermoclines and long-term climatic change; the ships mainly involved in taking XBT soundings are warships, research vessels, weather ships and those involved in dedicated scientific projects such as TOGA (Tropical Ocean and Global Atmosphere Programme).

CHAPTER 3

GENERAL METEOROLOGICAL INSTRUMENTS

Instruments for the measurement of almost every meteorological element have been developed for land stations, with the notable exception of cloud type and amount. These, being purely subjective observations, can only be assessed by human interpretation. Unfortunately, many of the instruments designed for use of land stations are unsuitable for operation with reasonable satisfaction on board ship. Special problems arise, not only from the motion of the vessel, its forward movement and exposure to saline spray, but also because of the disturbances created by the ship itself in the surrounding atmosphere.

In consequence, methods suitable to land stations would be at best merely an unnecessary expense at sea, and at worst would soon fail to operate or give misleading results. Rather than receive inaccurate data which cannot be verified, forecasters and climatologists would prefer to receive no data. For example, a hair hygrograph, an instrument giving a continuous recording of the relative humidity of the air, relies upon the change of length of a bundle of human hairs for its operation. In addition to the adverse effect of ship's movement upon the light and delicate pen movement, the existence of salt upon the hairs would seriously affect their readings.

Pressure, temperature and humidity have been covered in the preceding chapters. For general interest the standard instruments for measuring the other normally observed elements are given below, without regard as to whether they might, in special circumstances, be adapted for shipboard use.

WIND SPEED AND DIRECTION

Anemometer
This consists of cups rotatable about a vertical shaft or a propeller rotating about a horizontal shaft. When driven by the wind at a speed proportional to wind force, the rotating shaft drives an electrical generator whose output is itself proportional to the speed of rotation. A voltmeter may thus be calibrated as wind speed. Anemometers are not normally used aboard merchant ships because of the difficulty of finding a suitable site and also because of expense. The UK Ocean Weather Ship carries anemometers on the yardarms at a suitable height above the water (23 m), which seems to be the site furthest from eddying effects. But even here estimates of wind force and direction from the appearance of the sea are regularly made as a check on the instruments. (See Figure 17).

Hand anemometer
Whilst estimates of wind force and direction made on merchant ships by observations of sea state are to be considered the norm, a hand-held anemometer can be used for verification or in sheltered waters where the appearance of the sea may be modified by topographic features. The hand anemometer is held with its

Figure 17.   Anemometer and wind vane.

axis vertical, at arm's length, with the arm at right angles to the wind direction to avoid disturbance of the airflow by the observer's body. At least two readings of mean wind speed need to be taken within the overall period of observation, each reading being taken over at least 15 seconds. The wind speed is shown by a graduated scale across which a pointer moves. Hand anemometers are calibrated in knots over a range of 0 to 60.

Digital hand anemometer
This is similar to the hand anemometer except that the speed sensing mechanism does not make use of switched contacts. After sampling for 15 seconds the instrument displays the average wind speed digitally for a further period of 10 seconds. The body and switch of the anemometer are waterproof and support legs fixed to the body protect the cups against damage when the instrument is laid down. The power is supplied by battery with an indication when battery voltage is low.

Wind vane
The wind direction may be directly observed by the position of the wind vane or remotely read at deck level by an electrical direction transmitter known as a Magslip for mains power or a Desynn in the case of a battery system operated through gear wheels and a countershaft. Both types may be joined to an anemometer unit so that the two instruments form a single transmitting head.

VISIBILITY

Visibility recorder or transmissometer
Light from a lamp of known output is transmitted over a prescribed distance parallel to the ground. It is then received by a calibrated photocell. The degree by which the light has been attenuated by mist or fog is thus observable. An alternative system, employing the increased amount of light scattered backwards towards the light when fog exists, is already in use in Trinity House lighthouses and automatic light vessels. Both methods depend upon optical systems and hence are unsuitable for the marine environment.

CLOUD HEIGHT

Cloud-height balloons.   Cloud height may be measured in daylight by determining the time taken by a small rubber balloon, inflated with hydrogen or helium, to rise from ground level to the base of the cloud. The rate of ascent of the balloon is determined mainly by the free lift of the balloon and can be adjusted by controlling the amount of hydrogen or helium in the balloon. The time of travel between release of the balloon and its entry into the cloud is measured by stop-watch. Cloud height is then calculated from the rate of ascent and the time taken for the balloon to rise to the cloud base.

Cloud searchlight
This method is normally only available at night. A purpose-built searchlight with a parabolic silvered-glass reflector, mounted in a strong cylindrical case and having three adjustable feet on the base for levelling purposes, is projected vertically on to the cloud base. The angle of elevation of the patch of light on the cloud base is measured by alidade, sextant or theodolite from a distant point, the optimum distance of separation being about 300 m (1000 ft). The cloud height can then be calculated by conversion of the angle of observation into a height in metres for a baseline of 300 m. On a dark overcast night, cloud heights up to about 3000 m (10 000 ft) can be measured with acceptable accuracy.

Cloud-base recorder
This is an automatic device in which the same principles are employed as for the cloud searchlight, in that the angle at which a projected beam of light meets the cloud is measured over a known baseline. In this automatic instrument, the light is 'modulated', i.e. it is interrupted at a known rate and a photocell, replacing the human eye, detects only this modulated light even in the presence of daylight. The cloud-base recorder can thus operate day and night and will provide a continuous record of cloud height from its own operation of the angle of sight measured by the photocell system. The complete system consists of three units: a transmitter, a receiver and a recorder. The transmitter and receiver are remotely switched from the recorder which may be positioned from the operating site by between 1 km and 24 km, depending on the model used. These recorders are being superseded by cloud-base recorders using a laser technique.

UPPER WINDS

Pilot-Balloon Ascent

Small helium-filled balloons, whose rate of ascent is predetermined, are tracked by optical theodolite. From a safety viewpoint, the use of hydrogen as a balloon-inflating medium is being phased out and is not used on board ship. From the observed bearings the horizontal movement of the balloon, and hence the wind, can be computed for each layer of the atmosphere through which the balloon passes. This method is rarely used nowadays in routine practice because of its limitations. The most significant drawback is the presence of cloud but it still serves a purpose at locations where cloud cover is minimal or where there is a specialized requirement at a particular location, e.g. gliding.

Wind-finding radar

In this instance the balloon carries a radar reflector, usually of metallized mesh or solid reflecting surfaces. The radar provides accurate readings of azimuth, elevation and slant range. In consequence the upper winds may be computed even when the balloon is invisible owing to cloud or fog. The use of radar enables upper winds to be determined on a routine basis to heights of 25 km or more. For shipboard use, radar poses special problems in that the radar platform needs stabilizing if the required accuracy is to be achieved: this is expensive and difficult and only specialized ships are fitted with stabilized radar platforms. Today's technology makes it possible to measure upper winds without radar but it requires an additional attachment (a radiosonde) to be flown on the balloon.

UPPER-AIR SOUNDINGS

Radiosonde

A device carried by hydrogen- or helium-filled balloons to make observations of pressure, temperature and humidity to heights generally between 25 km and 30 km and to transmit these observations to a ground station by radio. (See Figure 18). There have been significant advances in the design and construction of such instruments in recent years; they are now smaller and lighter and the derivation of the results, after being received by the ground station, is carried out by a small computer. This also encodes and sends results in an internationally recognized WMO format. These data are an essential input into the mathematical models upon which modern forecasts are based.

The determination of upper winds without radar is achieved by the addition of some electronics both to the radiosonde and ground station and then utilizing the general availability of either OMEGA or LORAN navigation signals. The ground station, either fixed or mobile, e.g. a ship, and the radiosonde, both receive the appropriate NAVAID transmissions. The radiosonde retransmits the data appropriate to its movement in response to the upper winds, and from this information the surface-based computer calculates the upper winds (in practice it is the phase shift which is detected). Such a process eliminates the need for a stabilized radar platform but does require the satisfactory reception of the appropriate NAVAID signals from a sufficient number of transmitters.

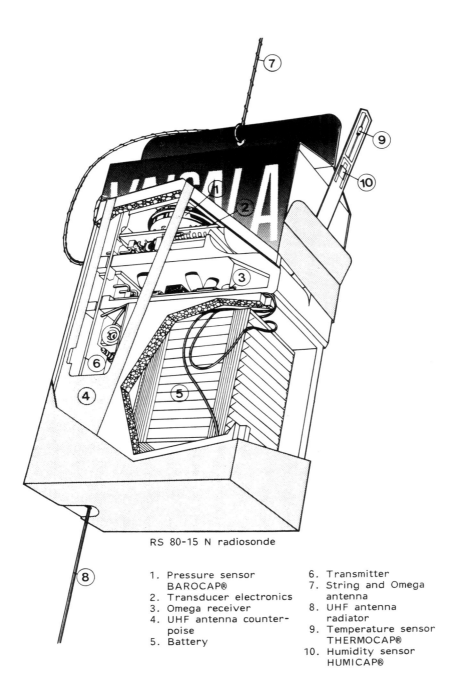

RS 80-15 N radiosonde

1. Pressure sensor
   BAROCAP®
2. Transducer electronics
3. Omega receiver
4. UHF antenna counter-
   poise
5. Battery

6. Transmitter
7. String and Omega
   antenna
8. UHF antenna
   radiator
9. Temperature sensor
   THERMOCAP®
10. Humidity sensor
    HUMICAP®

Figure 18.   Radiosonde instrument.

With the degree of automation now achieved and the ability to determine upper winds, merchant ships on passage can undertake this type of work. This is known as the Automated Shipboard Aerological Programme.

Automated Shipboard Aerological Programme
ASAP is a method of obtaining upper-air information from a merchant ship on passage. The system, as conceived by the Canadian Atmospheric Environment Service in 1982 and now used operationally, utilizes a fitted 20-foot container secured to the deck abaft the bridge. The container is divided into two sections, one section housing the computerized ground equipment and the other an automated balloon launcher. Power is supplied from the ship's alternators and transformed to the required voltage; the computer and other units receive power through an inverter with battery back-up.

The method of operation is comparatively simple: the balloon is inflated with helium inside a fibreglass drum which is attached to a hydraulically or electrically operated lifting mechanism. The sonde package is attached to the balloon by way of a small door in the drum; the latter is then raised through an opening in the deckhead of the container, tilted and the balloon ejected by air from an attached compressor. Signals from the sonde are received by aerials rigged above the bridge and relayed to the computer, which processes the information and codes it into a standard format. The coded message is then transferred to a Data Collection Platform which transmits it via satellite at pre-fixed time-slots.

Since the introduction of ASAP to UK Voluntary Observing Fleet ships in 1987, the only major change made to the original installation has been the addition of a portable balloon-launcher: the balloon is filled in the launcher and released by hand on the lee side of the ship, thus obviating the need for course alterations in unfavourable wind conditions. The present containerized version will eventually be replaced by a distributed system in which the receiving equipment will be housed on the bridge and all balloon launches made from portable launchers secured at suitable locations on the afterdeck. Although the UK has now ceased ASAP operations, several other countries operate similar systems; two ASAP units deployed on board ships of the French VOF utilize this configuration. In most cases a professional meteorologist is provided on board to operate the ASAP system.

CHAPTER 4

WIND, WEATHER AND VISIBILITY

Introduction

Non-instrumental observations are very important and, being estimates, they are dependent upon the personal judgement of the observer. This judgement is the product of training and experience at sea, together with practice in making the observations. To acquire a technique of observation, adherence to the official instructions is essential. The aim of these instructions is not only to outline a satisfactory method of making observations, but also to impose a standard procedure such that two observers, despite differences in training, will make approximately the same observation in similar circumstances. The assumption that observations are comparable, or made according to the same procedure, is the basis of synoptic meteorology or of a study of climate.

Observations from ships are of special importance to the forecaster not only because they enable him to complete his charts over the oceans, but also because weather sequences at sea are simpler than those on land. They are therefore more characteristic of the air masses and hence more useful in the air-mass analysis that precedes the preparation of forecasts. Numerous instances occur in which the presence or absence of adequate ship reports has made all the difference between good and bad weather forecasts. An observer should never forget that his individual effort, his particular observations, may supply just the information required to resolve a forecasting problem hundreds or thousands of miles away.

The making of meteorological observations at sea is attended by many difficulties that are unknown to the observer on shore. It is in overcoming them that the experience and training of the mariner are important. These difficulties largely result from the movement of the ship and the absence of landmarks.

Wind force and direction

Wind force is expressed numerically on a scale from 0 to 12 (see note to Table 10). This scale, which originally defined the wind force in terms of the canvas carried by a frigate, was devised by Captain, afterwards Admiral, Sir Francis Beaufort in the year 1806 for use in vessels of the Royal Navy. Since Admiral Beaufort's time, however, so many changes had taken place in the build, rig, and tonnage of seagoing vessels that in 1874 Beaufort's scale was adapted to the full-rigged ship with double topsails of that period. With the passing of sail, this specification meant very little to those who had no experience in square-rigged ships, and the practice arose of judging wind force from the state of the sea surface. In 1939 the International Meteorological Organization, now the WMO, agreed to the use of a sea criterion by which the wind force was judged from the appearance of the sea surface. This specification, brought into use in 1941, is shown on pages 38 and 39. Photographs showing the appearance of the sea corresponding to each Beaufort force are given on pages 40 to 47.

37

BEAUFORT SCALE OF WIND FORCE

Beaufort scale number	Mean wind speed		Limits of wind speed		Descriptive terms	Sea criterion	Probable height of waves in metres*	Probable maximum height of waves in metres*
	knots	metres per second	knots	metres per second				
	Measured at a height of 10 metres above sea level							
0	00	0.0	Less than 1	0.0–0.2	Calm	Sea like mirror.	—	—
1	02	0.8	1–3	0.3–1.5	Light air	Ripples with the appearance of scales are formed but without foam crests	0.1	0.1
2	05	2.4	4–6	1.6–3.3	Light breeze	Small wavelets, still short but more pronounced; crests have a glassy appearance and do not break.	0.2	0.3
3	09	4.3	7–10	3.4–5.4	Gentle breeze	Large wavelets. Crests begin to break. Foam of glassy appearance. Perhaps scattered white horses.	0.6	1.0
4	13	6.7	11–16	5.5–7.9	Moderate breeze	Small waves, becoming longer; fairly frequent white horses.	1.0	1.5
5	19	9.3	17–21	8.0–10.7	Fresh breeze	Moderate waves, taking a more pronounced long form; many white horses are formed. (Chance of some spray.)	2.0	2.5
6	24	12.3	22–27	10.8–13.8	Strong breeze	Large waves begin to form; the white foam crests are more extensive everywhere. (probably some spray.)	3.0	4.0
7	30	15.5	28–33	13.9–17.1	Near gale	Sea heaps up and white foam from breaking waves begins to be blown in streaks along the direction of the wind.	4.0	5.5
8	37	18.9	34–40	17.2–20.7	Gale	Moderately high waves of greater length; edges of crests begin to break into spindrift. The foam is blown in well-marked streaks along the direction of the wind.	5.5	7.5

BEAUFORT SCALE OF WIND FORCE — *continued*

Beaufort scale number	Mean wind speed		Limits of wind speed		Descriptive terms	Sea criterion	Probable height of waves in metres*	Probable maximum height of waves in metres*
	knots	metres per second	knots	metres per second				
		Measured at a height of 10 metres above sea level						
9	44	22.6	41–47	20.8–24.4	Strong gale	High waves. Dense streaks of foam along the direction of the wind. Crests of waves begin to topple, tumble and roll over. Spray may affect visibility.	7.0	10.0
10	52	26.4	48–55	24.5–28.4	Storm	Very high waves with long overhanging crests. The resulting foam in great patches is blown in dense white streaks along the direction of the wind. On the whole the surface of the sea takes on a white appearance. The tumbling of the sea becomes heavy and shocklike. Visibility affected.	9.0	12.5
11	60	30.5	56–63	28.5–32.6	Violent storm	Exceptionally high waves. (Small and medium-sized ships might be for a time lost to view behind the waves.) The sea is completely covered with long white patches of foam lying along the direction of the wind. Everywhere the edges of the wave crests are blown into froth. Visibility affected.	11.5	16.0
12	—	—	64 and over	32.7 and over	Hurricane	The air is filled with foam and spray. Sea completely white with driving spray; visibility very seriously affected.	14 and over	—

* These columns are added as a guide to show roughly what may be expected in the open sea, remote from land. In enclosed waters, or when near land with an off-shore wind, wave heights will be smaller and the waves steeper.

NOTES: — (a) It must be realized that it will be difficult at night to estimate wind force by the sea criterion.

(b) The lag effect between the wind getting up and the sea increasing should be borne in mind.

(c) Fetch, depth, swell, heavy rain and tide effects should be considered when estimating the wind force from the appearance of the sea.

N.C. Horner

Force 0

Wind speed less than 1 kn. (Sea like a mirror.)

G.J. Simpson

Force 1

Wind speed 1–3 kn; mean, 2 kn. (Ripples with the appearance of scales are formed, but without foam crests.)

Force 2

Wind speed 4–6 kn; mean, 5 kn. (Small wavelets, still short, but more pronounced; crests have a glassy appearance and do not break.)

Force 3

Wind speed 7–10 kn; mean 9 kn. (Large wavelets; crests begin to break. Foam of glassy appearance; perhaps scattered white horses.)

I.G. MacNeil

Force 4

Wind speed 11–16 kn; mean 13 kn. (Small waves, becoming longer; fairly frequent white horses.)

I.G. MacNeil

Force 5

Wind speed 17–21 kn; mean 19 kn. (Moderate waves, taking a more pronounced long form; many white horses are formed. Chance of some spray.)

Force 6

Wind speed 22–27 kn; mean 24 kn. (Large waves begin to form; the white foam crests are more extensive everywhere. Probably some spray.)

Force 7

Wind speed 28–33 kn; mean 30 kn. (Sea heaps up and white foam from breaking waves begins to be blown in streaks along the direction of the wind.)

W.A.E. Smith

Force 8

Wind speed 34–40 kn; mean 37 kn. (Moderately high waves of greater length; edges of crests begin to break into spindrift. The foam is blown in well-marked streaks along the direction of the wind.)

J.P. Laycock

Force 9

Wind speed 41–47 kn; mean 44 kn. (High waves. Dense streaks of foam along the direction of the wind. Crests of waves begin to topple, tumble and roll over. Spray may affect visibility.)

J.P. Laycock

G. Allen

Force 10

Wind speed 48–55 kn; mean 52 kn. (Very high waves with long overhanging crests. The resulting foam, in great patches, is blown in dense white streaks along the direction of the wind. The sea surface takes on a white appearance as a whole. The tumbling of the sea becomes heavy and shock-like. Visibility is affected.)

(The upper and lower photographs illustrate the difference in appearance between seas viewed almost along the wind direction and along the trough respectively.)

Crown copyright

Crown copyright

Force 11

Wind speed 56–63 kn; mean 60 kn. (Exceptionally high waves. The sea is completely covered with long white patches of foam lying along the direction of the wind. Everywhere the edges of the wave crests are blown into froth. Visibility is affected and small- and medium-sized ships may be lost from view behind the waves.)

Force 12

Wind speed 64–71 kn; mean 68 kn. The Beaufort Scale of wind force extends up to Force 17 (up to 118 kn), but Force 12 is the highest which can be identified from the appearance of the sea. (The air is filled with foam and spray. Sea completely white with driving spray; visibility very seriously affected.)

In using this specification it is assumed that the observation is made in the open ocean and that the wind has been blowing long enough to raise the appropriate sea. The possibility of a lag between the wind getting up and the sea increasing must be considered. The appearance of the sea surface also depends on many other factors such as the fetch of the wind (i.e. distance from weather shore), the swell, the presence of tides, and whether or not precipitation is occurring. These effects should be allowed for before deciding the appropriate number on the scale. Experience is the only sure guide but the following remarks may be of some use:

(a) A discrepancy between wind and sea occurs frequently close inshore where winds of a local character are likely.

(b) An off-shore wind does not produce its appropriate sea close inshore but requires a certain fetch before its full effect is produced.

(c) Swell is the name given to waves, generally of considerable length, raised by winds at a considerable distance from the point of observation. Swell is not taken into account when estimating wind.

(d) Tides or strong currents affect the appearance of the sea surface, a wind against tide or current causing more 'lop' — a weather tide — and the wind in the same direction as a tide or current producing less disturbance of the sea surface — a lee tide.

(e) Precipitation, especially if heavy, produces a smoothing effect on the sea surface.

(f) There is evidence that the height of the sea disturbance caused by a wind of a particular force is affected by the difference between sea and air temperatures, the sea being the warmer medium. If this difference increases, there is an appreciable increase in the sea disturbance, and vice versa.

Beaufort force can be transformed approximately into wind speed by means of a table of equivalents included in the specification of Beaufort force given on pages 38 and 39.

The International Code (used for making meteorological reports by radio) makes provision for the reporting of wind speed in knots (or metres per second). The observer may derive this from the table of equivalents, taking the mid-point of the range corresponding with the observed Beaufort force; or, better still, he may interpolate according to his own judgement. For example, if the wind is estimated to be over Beaufort 5 but not quite Beaufort 6, it might be reported as having a mean speed of 21 knots.

Wind direction is logged as the true direction and is given to the nearest ten degrees. The exposed position that a ship's standard compass usually occupies gives a clear all-round view and from it the observer takes a compass bearing, noting the tops of the waves, the ripples, the spray and the faint lines that generally show along the wind. It is usually best to look to windward in judging wind direction, but in some lights the direction is more evident when looking to leeward.

Meteorologists as well as seamen use the term 'veering' to indicate a change of wind in a clockwise direction and the term 'backing' to denote a change in an anticlockwise direction.

Estimation of wind force and direction can often be made in the same way at night but sometimes on very dark nights it is impossible to see the effect of the lighter winds on the sea surface. In such cases, the apparent or relative wind force and direction must be estimated by their effect, i.e. by the 'feel' upon the face or upon a moistened finger, or by the direction in which the smoke is blowing. Allowance must then be made for the ship's course and speed. In a fast ship considerable difference exists between the apparent and true wind directions. When the wind is astern and of the same velocity as the ship there is apparent calm on board the ship. In a calm, a ship steaming at 10 knots will have an apparent head wind of velocity 10 knots, but as soon as the wind blows from any direction out of the fore and aft line, the difference between the apparent and true directions will vary with each angle on the bow, and with each force of the wind. The true wind may be obtained from the apparent wind by use of the parallelogram of velocities, or Table 10 as explained below. In Figure 19 if, for example, the ship is travelling along the line AB with speed 15 knots and the wind appears to be coming from the direction DA with speed 29 knots (Beaufort scale 7), the true direction of the wind is along CA and its speed 18 knots.

This result is easily obtained graphically by drawing the figure, making BA proportional to 15 and DA proportional to 29, and then measuring DB which is equal to CA, where ABDC is a parallelogram. The angle CAD, which is the same as BDA, is measured with a protractor and gives the difference between the true and apparent directions of the wind. Table 10 enables the conversion from apparent to true wind to be made by inspection.

In fast vessels the task of estimating accurately the true wind force and direction is no easy one and special care is required; this applies particularly to occasions when the wind is very light, and on dark nights.

Anemometers have as yet found only limited use at sea, the chief problem being to achieve a suitable exposure. Estimation of wind force and direction from careful observation of the sea state is the method preferred. The ship disturbs the airflow in its vicinity with the result that the wind measured by the instrument is not representative of the true airflow over the open sea. If a portable cup-anemometer is used, the exposure may be varied at will and the best position chosen for any particular wind direction. The instrument measures 'apparent' wind speed. To determine the true value, the wind direction must first be estimated and then allowance made for the speed of the ship.

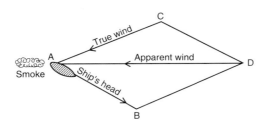

Figure 19.   Wind, parallelogram of velocities.

Wind force and direction, taken alone, do not completely specify the character of the wind. It is well known that on occasions the wind is particularly gusty, as in showery weather. Less frequently, definite squalls may occur. The difference between a gust and a squall is essentially one of time-scale, a gust being momentary, whereas a squall may last several minutes. It is important when making the observations to note any unusual gustiness and the occurrence of squalls. When the latter occur it is of advantage if the time be noted together with any sudden change in wind direction. It is of interest to note that gusts have no appreciable effect in raising waves, whereas squalls may act for a sufficient length of time to raise a group of waves which tend to travel with the squall.

WEATHER

For the purposes of the meteorological logbook, the term 'weather' embraces those elements covered by the 'present weather' and 'past weather' codes, i.e. fog, precipitation, etc. (see Met.O.509, *Ships' Code and Decode Book*).

For a concise description of weather, Admiral Beaufort devised a system known as the Beaufort notation. Since 1958 this method has not been used to record weather at the synoptic hour but it is given below as it provides a handy way of amplifying the main synoptic report, or of recording the weather between observations, e.g. duration of precipitation, in the remarks column of the meteorological logbook for research purposes. It may also be found useful in the Deck Logbook and in the plotting of weather bulletins.

The present codes are sufficient to describe the weather for synoptic purposes, and they are also suitable for data processing by computer or by other machine methods.

The Beaufort notation

Weather	Beaufort letter	Weather	Beaufort letter
Blue sky (0–2/8 clouded)	b	Overcast sky (unbroken cloud covering sky)	o
Sky partly clouded (3–5/8 clouded)	bc	Squally weather	q
Cloudy (6–8/8 clouded)	c	Rain	r
Drizzle	d	Sleet (rain and snow together)	rs
Wet air (without precipitation)	e	Snow	s
Fog	f	Thunder	t
Gale	g	Thunderstorm with rain	tlr
Hail	h	Thunderstorm with snow	tls
Precipitation in sight of ship or station	jp	Ugly threatening sky	u
Line squall	kq	Unusual visibility	v
Storm of drifting snow	ks	Dew	w
Sandstorm or duststorm	kz	Hoar-frost	x
Lightning	l	Dry air	y
Mist	m	Dust haze	z

The system has been extended since Beaufort's day to provide indication of intensity and continuity. Capital letters are now used to indicate occasions when the phenomenon noted is intense. On the other hand, occasions of slight intensity are distinguished by adding a small suffix 'o'.

50

Thus R   = Heavy rain
      r   = Moderate rain
      r_o = Slight rain.

The prefix 'i' indicates 'intermittent', thus:
    if   = Fog patches.
    ir_o = Intermittent slight rain.
The prefix 'p' indicates 'shower of', thus:
    pR   = Shower of heavy rain.
    ps_o = Shower of slight snow.

A solidus '/' is used in 'present weather' to distinguish present conditions from those in the past hour, thus:

    c/r_o = Cloudy after slight rain in the past hour.
Continuity is indicated by repeating the letter, thus:
    rr   = Continuous moderate rain.
The following are further examples of the use of Beaufort notation:
    cs_os_o = Cloudy with continuous slight snow.
    oid_o = Overcast with intermittent slight drizzle.
    bif   = Blue sky with fog patches.
    cqprh   = Cloudy with squalls and shower of moderate rain and hail.
    crrm   = Cloudy with continuous moderate rain, and mist.

In past weather the letters are used in the same way but their order from left to right indicates sequence in time.

Thus 'b, bc, cpr' indicates cloudless conditions, becoming partly cloudy, followed by cloudy conditions with shower(s) of rain.

Precipitation
A distinction is drawn in the present and past weather codes between rain, drizzle and showers. Showers are of short duration and the fair periods between them are characterized by clearances of the sky. Showers fall from clouds having great vertical extent and usually isolated. They do not often last more than half an hour. Showers are characteristic of an unstable polar air mass, usually flowing in the rear of a depression, but they are by no means confined to this situation.

Rain and drizzle fall from overcast or nearly overcast skies. The distinction between rain and drizzle depends not on the amount of the precipitation but on the size of the drops. Drizzle is 'precipitation in which the drops are very small' (diameter less than 0.5 mm). Slight rain, on the other hand, is precipitation in which the drops are of appreciable size (they may even be large drops), but are relatively few in number. Observers should decide from the size of the drops whether the precipitation is drizzle or rain, and from the combined effect of the number and size of the drops whether the precipitation is slight, moderate or heavy. The description 'heavy' is relatively rare in temperate latitudes.

Precipitation is defined as intermittent if it has been discontinuous during the preceding hour, without presenting the character of a shower. Observers should cultivate the practice of recording the times of onset and cessation of precipitation.

Fog, mist and haze

Fog, mist and haze have in the past been used, rather loosely, to describe decreasing degrees of obscurity in the atmosphere. Modern practice reserves the description 'haze' for occasions when the obscurity is caused by solid particles such as dust or sea salt. Fog and mist are akin in that they are both composed of minute water drops and may thus be distinguished from haze. In practice the distinction is usually made by means of the dry- and wet-bulb readings. The following table gives the approximate criterion for the reporting of mist and haze at various temperatures. Intermediate values may be obtained by interpolation. If the depression of the wet-bulb is more than about that shown in the relevant column B, haze should be reported. If the depression is less, the obscurity should be reported as mist. In the case of the UK Met. Office, a relative humidity of 95 per cent is used as a guide to the dividing line between mist and haze.

DEPRESSION OF THE WET BULB CORRESPONDING TO A RELATIVE
HUMIDITY OF 95%

Column A	Columns B	
	Depression °C	
Dry-Bulb °C	Stevenson screen	Aspirated psychrometer
40	0.8	0.8
35	0.7	0.7
30	0.7	0.7
25	0.6	0.6
20	0.5	0.6
15	0.5	0.5
10	0.4	0.4
5	0.3	0.3
0	0.3	0.3

The further distinction between mist and fog is only one of degree and is arbitrarily assigned. When the visibility is reduced to less than 1 km or 0.54 n. mile the obscurity is described as fog; when greater than 1 km it is known as mist.

Visibility

Although the use of such terms as fog, mist and haze is suitable for a general indication of the state of visibility in the WW code or in the text of a ship's logbook, a more precise method is needed in weather messages to indicate to the meteorologist the degree of obscurity of the atmosphere, irrespective of the reason that causes it. On land, observations are made of a number of selected objects at fixed distances, the distances increasing roughly in such a way that each distance is nearly double the next smaller distance. The determination of the most distant object of the series which is visible on any given occasion constitutes the observation of visibility. At sea such a detailed determination of visibility is not usually possible, but in making estimates of visibility a coarser scale is used, as shown below.

VISIBILITY SCALE FOR USE AT SEA

Code figure		Code figure	
90	Less than 50 m	95	1.1 n. mile or 2 km
91	50 m	96	2.2 n. mile or 4 km
92	0.11 n. mile or 200 m	97	5.4 n. mile or 10 km
93	0.27 n. mile or 500 m	98	10.8 n. mile or 20 km
94	0.54 n. mile or 1 km	99	27.0 n. mile or 50 km

Note 1: If the distance of visibility is between two of the distances given in the table, the code figure for the shorter distance is reported.

Note 2: The prefix '9' before each of the scale numbers appears here because this table is part of a code for reporting visibility in two figures by radio (see Met.O.509, *Ship's Code and Decode Book*, or *Admiralty List of Radio Signals*, Volume 3).

In a long vessel the determination of the lowest numbers offers no difficulty as objects at known distances may be used. Visibility numbers in the middle range indicate conditions of obscurity such that the visibility is greater than the length of the ship but is not sufficient to allow full speed to be maintained. The only means of obtaining observations for the higher numbers of the scale are as follows. When coasting and when fixes can be obtained, the distance of points when first sighted, or last seen may be measured, from the chart. In the open sea, when other ships are sighted, visibility may be estimated by noting the radar range when the vessel is first sighted visually and again when it disappears from view. It is customary to use the horizon to estimate visibility numbers in the higher range although this cannot be relied upon. There are cases of abnormal refraction when the visible horizon may be very misleading as a means of judging distances, particularly when the height of the eye is great, as in the case of an observer on the bridge of a large vessel.

The estimation of visibility at night is very difficult. What the meteorologist is interested in knowing is the degree of transparency of the atmosphere. But the distance seen at night depends on the amount of illumination; and the distance at which a light is seen depends on its intensity or candle-power. If there is no obvious change in meteorological conditions, the visibility just after dark will be the same as that recorded just before dark irrespective of the fact that one may not be able to see as far. A deterioration in visibility can sometimes be detected afterwards and the visibility figure adjusted accordingly. In doing this, care must be taken not to confuse the effect of a decrease in illumination, as for example when the moon sets, with a genuine decrease in visibility. The presence of a 'loom' around the vessel's navigation lights is frequently a guide to deteriorating visibility.

CHAPTER 5

CLOUDS AND CLOUD HEIGHT BY ESTIMATION

A normal observation of cloud at sea involves:

(a)　The identification of the cloud types present.
(b)　An estimation of the height of the base of the lowest cloud in the sky.
(c)　An estimation of the amount of all cloud of type C_L (or C_M, if no C_L).

The fundamental distinction in structure which has great significance for forecasting, is between 'layer' or 'sheet' clouds, and 'heap' clouds, i.e. clouds with marked vertical development. Examples of the latter are cumulus, sometimes known as the 'wool pack' or 'cauliflower' cloud, and cumulonimbus, the 'thundercloud' or 'anvil' cloud. In the further classification of sheet or layer clouds the consideration of height is taken into account, but the classification is not strictly one of height so much as of appearance. The main classification is into ten types as follows:

Sheet clouds		*Approximate limits (see also page 61)*
Cirrus	(Ci)	
Cirrocumulus	(Cc)	Base above 18 000 feet (5500 m)
Cirrostratus	(Cs)	
Altocumulus	(Ac)	6500 to 18 000 feet (2000 to 5500 m)
Altostratus	(As)	
Nimbostratus	(Ns)	
Stratocumulus	(Sc)	
Stratus	(St)	
		Base below 6500 feet (2000 m)
Heap clouds (with vertical development)		
Cumulus	(Cu)	
Cumulonimbus	(Cb)	

Descriptions of the different types are given below.

Cirrus (Ci)
Detached clouds of delicate and fibrous appearance, without shading, generally white in colour, often of a silky appearance. Cirrus appears in the most varied forms, such as isolated tufts, lines drawn across a blue sky, branching feather-like plumes and curved lines ending in tufts. These lines are often arranged in bands which cross the sky in lines and which, owing to the effect of perspective, appear to converge to a point on the horizon, or to two opposite points (i.e. polar bands). Cirrostratus and cirrocumulus often take part in the formation of these bands. Before sunrise and after sunset, cirrus is sometimes coloured bright yellow or red. Owing to their great height cirriform clouds are illuminated long before other

clouds and fade out much later. Observation of cirrus at night is difficult but, if thick and extensive, it may be noted by its dimming effect on stars.

Cirrocumulus (Cc)

A cirriform layer or patch composed of small white flakes or of very small globular masses, without shadows, which are arranged in groups or lines, or more often in ripples resembling those of the sand on the seashore.

In general, cirrocumulus represents a degraded state of cirrus and cirrostratus, both of which may change into it. In this case the changing patches often retain some fibrous structures in places. Real cirrocumulus is uncommon. It must not be confused with small altocumulus on the edges of altocumulus sheets. In the absence of any other criterion the term cirrocumulus should only be used when:

(a)   there is evident connection with cirrus or cirrostratus, or
(b)   the cloud observed results from a change in cirrus or cirrostratus.

Cirrostratus (Cs)

A thin whitish veil, which does not blur the outlines of the sun or moon, but gives rise to haloes. Sometimes it is quite diffuse and merely gives the sky a milky look; sometimes it more or less distinctly shows a fibrous structure with disordered filaments. Cirrostratus may be observed at night by noting the slight diffusion of light around each star, whose brilliance is at the same time dimmed. It is almost impossible to differentiate between thick cirrus and cirrostratus at night in the absence of moonlight.

Altocumulus (Ac)

A layer or patches, composed of laminae or rather flattened globular masses, the smallest elements of the regularly arranged layers being fairly small and thin, with or without shading. These elements are arranged in groups, in lines, or waves, following one or two directions and are sometimes so close together that their edges join.

When the edge or a thin translucent patch of altocumulus passes in front of the sun or moon a corona appears. This phenomenon may also occur with cirrocumulus and with the higher forms of stratocumulus. Irisation or iridescence is another possibility with altocumulus. (See also pages 164 and 175.)

The limits within which altocumulus is met are very wide. At the greatest heights, when made up of small elements, it resembles cirrocumulus; altocumulus, however, is distinguished by not being either closely associated with cirrus or cirrostratus or evolved from one of these types. It is often associated with altostratus and either form may change into the other.

Two important varieties of altocumulus are 'altocumulus castellanus' and 'altocumulus lenticularis'. Altocumulus castellanus is a variety peculiar to a thundery state of the atmosphere, and is sure evidence of high-level instability. In this form individual cloudlets are extended vertically upwards in heads or towers, like small cumuli. The lenticular variety of altocumulus has clouds of an ovoid or lens shape, with clear-cut edges and sometimes showing irisation. It occurs frequently over mountainous country and in 'föhn', 'scirocco' and 'mistral' winds. It may also often be seen after the passage of weak cold fronts.

Altostratus (As)

Striated or fibrous veil, more or less grey or bluish in colour. This colour is like thick cirrostratus, but does not show halo phenomena; the sun or moon shows vaguely, with a gleam, as though through ground glass. Sometimes the sheet is thin with forms intermediate with cirrostratus. Sometimes it is very thick and dark, perhaps even completely obscuring the sun or moon. In this case differences of thickness may cause relatively light patches between very dark parts; but the surface never shows real relief, and the striated or fibrous structure is always seen in places in the body of the cloud. Every gradation is observed between high altostratus and cirrostratus on the one hand and low altostratus and nimbostratus on the other. In practice it is important to distinguish between altostratus (thin) through which the sun or moon is visible and altostratus (thick) which completely obscures the sun or moon.

Nimbostratus (Ns)

A low, amorphous (i.e. without form), and rainy layer, of a dark-grey colour and nearly uniform; feebly illuminated seemingly from inside. Precipitation from nimbostratus is nearly always 'continuous'; but precipitation is not a sufficient criterion. Cloud may be described as nimbostratus before precipitation has started. There is often precipitation which does not reach the ground; in this case the base of the cloud is always diffuse and looks 'wet' on account of the general trailing precipitation, 'virga' (Latin — streak, bough or broom) so that it is not possible to determine precisely the limit of its lower surface.

Nimbostratus is usually the result of a progressive lowering and thickening of a layer of altostratus. Beneath nimbostratus there is generally a progressive development of very low ragged clouds (scud). These clouds are usually referred to as stratus fractus (St fra).

Stratus (St)

A uniform layer of cloud, resembling fog but not resting on the ground. When this very low layer is broken up into irregular shreds it is designated stratus fractus (St fra). A veil of true stratus generally gives the sky a hazy appearance which is very characteristic, but which in certain cases may cause confusion with nimbostratus. When there is precipitation the difference is manifest; stratus cannot give the continuous precipitation usually associated with nimbostratus. When there is no precipitation a dark and uniform layer of stratus can easily be mistaken for nimbostratus. The lower surface of nimbostratus, however, always has a wet appearance (widespread trailing precipitation or virga); it is quite uniform and it is not possible to make out definite details. Stratus on the other hand has a 'drier' appearance and, however uniform it may be, it shows some contrasts and some lighter transparent parts. Stratus is often a local cloud and, when it breaks up, the blue sky is often seen.

A common mode of stratus formation is the slow lifting of a fog layer due to increase in wind speed or warming of the surface.

Stratocumulus (Sc)

A layer or patches composed of rounded masses or rolls; the smallest of the regularly arranged elements are fairly large; they are soft and grey, with darker parts. These elements are arranged in groups, in lines, or in waves, aligned in one or two directions. Very often the rolls are so close that their edges join together; when they cover the whole sky as on the continent, especially in winter, they have a wavy appearance. The difference between stratocumulus and altocumulus is essentially one of height. A cloud sheet called altocumulus by an observer at a lower height may appear as stratocumulus to an observer at a considerably greater height.

Stratocumulus may form by the spreading out of cumulus. This happens over land in the evening when the daytime cumulus clouds begin to spread out prior to dissolving. Another example is when developing cumulus meets a pronounced inversion layer. If unable to penetrate this layer the cloud spreads out horizontally in the form of stratocumulus.

Cumulus (Cu)

Thick clouds with vertical development; the upper surface is dome-shaped and exhibits rounded protuberances, while the base is nearly horizontal. When the cloud is opposite to the sun the surfaces normal to the observer are brighter than the edges of the protuberances. When the light comes from the side the clouds exhibit strong contrasts of light and shade; against the sun, on the other hand, they look dark with a bright edge. True cumulus is definitely limited above and below, and its surface often appears hard and clear-cut; but one may also observe a cloud resembling ragged cumulus in which the different parts show constant change. This cloud is called cumulus fractus (Cu fra). Cumulus, whose base is horizontal, clear-cut and generally of a grey colour, has a uniform structure, that is to say it is composed of rounded parts right up to its summit, with no fibrous structure. One of the species of cumulus, cumulus congestus, can produce abundant precipitation in the tropics. As cumulonimbus generally results from development and transformation of cumulus, it is sometimes difficult to distinguish cumulus with great vertical extent from cumulonimbus. If it is not possible to decide on the basis of other criteria, the cloud should, by convention, be called cumulus if it is not accompanied by thunder, lightning or hail.

Cumulus having but small vertical development and little individual extent is known as 'fair-weather' cumulus' to distinguish it from the ordinary 'large cumulus'.

Cumulonimbus (Cb)

Heavy masses of cloud, with great vertical development whose cumuliform summits rise in the form of mountains or towers, the upper parts having a fibrous texture and often spreading out in the shape of an anvil. The base of the cloud resembles nimbostratus, and one generally notices 'virga' (trailing precipitation). This base has often a layer of very low ragged clouds below it.

Cumulonimbus clouds generally produce showers of rain or snow, and sometimes of hail or soft hail, and often thunderstorms as well. If the whole of the cloud cannot be seen, the fall of a moderate or heavy shower is enough to characterize the cloud as a cumulonimbus. A cumulonimbus cloud may cover the whole sky, in which case the base alone is visible and resembles nimbostratus from which it is difficult to distinguish it. If the cloud mass does not cover all the sky and if even small portions of the upper parts of the cumulonimbus appear, the difference is evident. In other cases the distinction can only be made if the preceding evolution of the clouds has been followed or if precipitation occurs. Cumulonimbus gives showers whereas nimbostratus is associated with continuous precipitation. When there is doubt as to the choice between cumulonimbus and cumulus, cumulonimbus should be reported if it is accompanied by lightning, thunder, or hail.

The lower surface of cumulonimbus sometimes has an udder-like or mamillated appearance which is referred to as 'mamma'. When a layer of menacing cloud covers the sky and mammatus structure and trailing precipitation are both seen, it is a sure sign that the cloud is the base of a cumulonimbus, even in the absence of all other signs.

The clouds which develop in the rear of depressions are often cumulonimbus. However, by the spreading out of the upper parts of this cloud and the dissolving of the lower parts, altocumulus or stratocumulus can form. Dense cirrus will develop when the cirriform upper parts of cumulonimbus spread out.

Making the observations
The aspect of the sky is continually changing and the cloud formations in evidence at one particular time may not be typical, that is to say they may not be easily recognizable from the standard descriptions given above. If, however, the observer watches the sky over a period of time he will often find that doubtful cloud forms may be referred to a previous state of development that was typical. Hence the first rule in cloud observing — watch the sky as often as possible and not merely at the time of observation.

Coding the observations
The forecaster who eventually receives and uses the observer's reports does not merely want to know what clouds are present. It has been found that certain distributions or arrangements of clouds in the sky, in other words certain 'states of sky', are of particular significance. The observer is required to report these rather than the presence of a particular cloud form. These states of sky are as follows, separate specifications being used for low, medium and high cloud.

SPECIFICATION OF FORM OF LOW CLOUD (C_L) (Sc, St, Cu, Cb)

Code
Figure

0	No Stratocumulus, Stratus, Cumulus or Cumulonimbus.
1	Cumulus with little vertical extent and seemingly flattened, or ragged Cumulus other than of bad weather*, or both.
2	Cumulus of moderate or strong vertical extent, generally with protuberances in the form of domes or towers, either accompanied or not by other Cumulus or by Stratocumulus, all having their bases at the same level.
3	Cumulonimbus the summits of which, at least partially, lack sharp outlines, but are neither clearly fibrous (cirriform) nor in the form of an anvil; Cumulus, Stratocumulus or Stratus may also be present.

*'Bad weather' denotes the conditions which generally exist during precipitation and a short time before and after.

4	Stratocumulus formed by the spreading out of Cumulus; Cumulus may also be present.
5	Stratocumulus not resulting from the spreading out of Cumulus.
6	Stratus in a more or less continuous sheet or layer, or in ragged shreds, or both, but no Stratus fractus of bad weather*.
7	Stratus fractus of bad weather* or Cumulus fractus of bad weather, or both, usually below Altostratus or Nimbostratus.
8	Cumulus and Stratocumulus other than that formed from the spreading out of Cumulus; the base of the Cumulus is at a different level from that of the Stratocumulus.
9	Cumulonimbus, the upper part of which is clearly fibrous (cirriform), often in the form of an anvil; either accompanied or not by Cumulonimbus without anvil or fibrous upper part, by Cumulus, Stratocumulus, Stratus or Stratus fractus.
/	Stratocumulus, Stratus, Cumulus and Cumulonimbus invisible owing to darkness, fog, blowing dust or sand, or other similar phenomena.

SPECIFICATION OF FORM OF MEDIUM CLOUD (C_M) (Ac, As, Ns)

Code figure

0	No Altocumulus, Altostratus or Nimbostratus.
1	Altostratus, the greater part of which is semi-transparent; through this part the sun or moon may be weakly visible, as through ground glass.
2	Altostratus, the greater part of which is sufficiently dense to hide the sun or moon, or Nimbostratus†.
3	Altocumulus, the greater part of which is semi-transparent; the various elements of the cloud change only slowly and are all at a single level.
4	Patches (often in the form of almonds or fishes) of Altocumulus, the greater part of which is semi-transparent; the clouds occur at one or more levels and elements are continually changing in appearance.
5	Semi-transparent Altocumulus in bands, or Altocumulus in one or more fairly continuous layers (semi-transparent or opaque), progressively invading the sky; these Altocumulus clouds generally thicken as a whole.
6	Altocumulus resulting from the spreading out of Cumulus (or Cumulonimbus).
7	Altocumulus in two or more layers usually opaque in places, and not progressively invading the sky; or opaque layer of Altocumulus, not progressively invading the sky; or Altocumulus together with Altostratus or Nimbostratus†.
8	Altocumulus with sproutings in the form of small towers or battlements, or Altocumulus having the appearance of cumuliform tufts.

*'Bad weather' denotes the conditions which generally exist during precipitation and a short time before and after.

†For synoptic purposes nimbostratus is included among the medium clouds in the code since it is continuous, with the altostratus existing above it, and has been formed as a result of a progressive lowering of altostratus from medium cloud level.

59

| 9 | Altocumulus of a chaotic sky, generally at several levels. |
| / | Altocumulus, Altostratus and Nimbostratus invisible owing to darkness, fog, blowing dust or sand or other similar phenomena, or more often because of the presence of a continuous layer of lower clouds. |

SPECIFICATION OF FORM OF HIGH CLOUD (C_H) (Ci, Cs, Cc)

Code figure

0	No Cirrus, Cirrocumulus or Cirrostratus.
1	Cirrus in the form of filaments, strands or hooks, not progressively invading the sky.
2	Dense Cirrus, in patches or entangled sheaves, which usually do not increase and sometimes seem to be the remains of the upper part of a Cumulonimbus; or Cirrus with sproutings in the form of small turrets or battlements, or Cirrus having the appearance of cumuliform tufts.
3	Dense Cirrus, often in the form of an anvil, being the remains of the upper parts of Cumulonimbus.
4	Cirrus in the form of hooks or of filaments, or both, progressively invading the sky; they generally become denser as a whole.
5	Cirrus (often in bands converging towards one point or two opposite points of the horizon) and Cirrostratus, or Cirrostratus alone; in either case, they are progressively invading the sky, and generally growing denser as a whole, but the continuous veil does not reach 45 degrees above the horizon.
6	Cirrus (often in bands converging towards one point or two opposite points of the horizon) and Cirrostratus, or Cirrostratus alone; in either case they are progressively invading the sky, and generally growing denser as a whole; the continuous veil extends more than 45 degrees above the horizon, without the sky being totally covered.
7	Veil of Cirrostratus covering the celestial dome.
8	Cirrostratus not progressively invading the sky and not completely covering the celestial dome.
9	Cirrocumulus alone, or Cirrocumulus accompanied by Cirrus or Cirrostratus, or both, but Cirrocumulus is predominant.
/	Cirrus, Cirrocumulus and Cirrostratus invisible owing to darkness, fog, blowing dust or sand or other similar phenomena, or more often because of the presence of a continuous layer of lower clouds.

The use of these specifications, instead of reporting each individual cloud form, effects an economy and is also advantageous to the forecaster, who knows how to associate a state of sky with a particular weather situation.

The estimation of cloud height
Apart from some ships of the Royal Navy and occasionally on ocean weather ships, cloud height at sea is obtained by estimation. The first step in estimating cloud height consists of identifying the cloud as a type belonging to one of the three

classes, low, medium or high. Low clouds have their bases below 6500 feet (2000 m). Medium cloud layers usually occur at levels between 6500 and 18 000 feet (2000 and 5500 m), and high clouds are usually above 18 000 feet (5500 m). As a rough guide, the heights of the bases of the various types of low cloud may be expected to be between the following limits:

Stratus	Usually below 2000 feet (600 m) and sometimes nearly down to the surface.
Nimbostratus	500 to 4000 feet (150 to 1200 m) usually below 2000 feet (600 m) in moderate rain or snow.
Cumulonimbus	2000 to 5000 feet (600 to 1500 m).
Stratocumulus	1500 to 4500 feet (450 to 1350 m).
Cumulus	1500 to 5000 feet (450 to 1500 m).

These limits tend to be considerably higher in low latitudes; this applies particularly to high clouds.

It is difficult to estimate cloud height without much practice. The apparent size of the cloud elements is often an indication of height. For example, the lower the height of the individual cloudlets of an altocumulus layer, the larger they will normally appear. Layers having the appearance of altocumulus with large individual elements are often found at heights between 6000 feet (1800 m) and 10 000 feet (3000 m). The estimation of the height of stratified cloud, e.g. altostratus or nimbostratus, is particularly difficult. The lack of pronounced structure makes it easy to gain a false impression of height. Valuable experience can be gained on occasions when the observer knows that his ship is steaming towards a depression by watching the gradual lowering of the cloud base. The observer's impressions of the appearance of the sky in the successive stages of lowering will assist his judgement on future occasions. It is only by such experience that an observer can distinguish between a layer of nimbostratus in the lower middle band and a similar layer at, perhaps, only 2000 to 3000 feet (600 to 900 m).

Care must be taken before using the apparent speed of cloud as an index to its height. This apparent speed depends not only on the velocity of the wind at cloud level but also on the course and speed of the ship itself.

When coasting, cloud height may sometimes be estimated by comparison with the height of the mountains or hills in the background. In using this method, however, it should be remembered that cloud is usually lower over the hills than elsewhere and that it is the general level over the sea that is required.

The estimation of cloud amount
The amount of cloud was in the past estimated as the number of tenths of sky covered. At a conference of the International Meteorological Organization (Washington 1947) it was recommended that amount of cloud be reported in eighths instead of tenths. This change of procedure was brought into force with the introduction of the revised International Code (Washington) on 1 January 1949.

In making the observation it is necessary to stand in a position affording an uninterrupted view of the whole sky. To make an estimate for the whole sky at once requires practice and is rather difficult at first. It is convenient to imagine the sky divided into quadrants by two arcs drawn at right angles through the zenith.

Each quadrant represents two-eighths of the total sky. If we choose the most appropriate of the figures —

    0 = Clear or almost clear of cloud
    1 = About half covered
    2 = Completely or almost completely covered with cloud —

for each separate quadrant, then the total amount of cloud for the whole sky is obtained simply by adding the amounts in the separate quadrants.

At night the observation of total cloud amount is noted by observing which stars are showing and which are obscured. It is more difficult to differentiate between low, middle and high clouds and reliable observation depends upon the degree of illumination and the experience of the observer.

C_L1 *Cumulus with little vertical extent.* The cloud elements shown in the upper picture are in an early stage of development: they are small, shallow and have ragged edges. In the lower picture they are in a slightly more advanced stage and some show the characteristic domed tops.

63

R.K. Pilsbury

R.K. Pilsbury

$C_L 2$ *Cumulus of moderate or strong vertical extent.* This is a further stage in the development of $C_L 1$. The cloud has become much deeper and the tops are 'cauliflower shaped'. The outlines are clear cut and there is no tendency for the upper parts of the cloud mass to become blurred or fibrous in texture. When the cloud is well developed, rain showers may occur. Stratocumulus cloud may also be present but it must be at the same level as the base of the Cumulus, as shown in the lower picture.

64

R.K. Pilsbury

R.K. Pilsbury

C_L3 *Cumulonimbus without anvil.*   Normally this is a further stage in the development of C_L2. The tops are beginning to acquire a fibrous appearance. When it is uncertain whether the cloud is C_L3 or C_L9, the latter should be selected if the cloud gives rise to lightning, thunder or hail. Cumulus, Stratocumulus or Stratus may also be present. The lower picture shows an extensive line of Cumulonimbus.

R.K. Pilsbury

R.K. Pilsbury

C_L4 *Stratocumulus formed by the spreading out of Cumulus.* Cloud of this type forms when the upper parts of Cumulus clouds, which had previously been gaining height, can no longer do so and begin to spread out horizontally, forming a layer of Stratocumulus, as shown in the upper picture. (See Page 77 describing the formation of C_M6.) Sometimes the spreading out is only temporary and the Cumulus resumes growth above the stable layer.

Another type of C_L4 often occurs in the evening when convection ceases and, in consequence, the Cumulus begins to flatten, and assumes the appearance of patches of Stratocumulus, as shown in the lower picture.

R.K. Pilsbury

R.K. Pilsbury

C_L5 *Stratocumulus not formed by the spreading out of Cumulus.* The individual cloud masses may be separate and in the form of elongated bands as shown in the upper picture, or they may be closed up into a continuous or nearly continuous layer, as shown in the lower picture. Often the cloud is dark and heavy looking, but it can also be light in tone when it is at a fairly high level, or when it is thin.

C$_L$6 *Stratus in a more or less continuous sheet or layer*, or in ragged shreds, or both. The upper picture shows a layer of Stratus with its base about 500 feet above sea level, just touching the cliff top. In the lower picture, the ragged Stratus was formed from lifted sea fog.

R.K. Pilsbury

R.K. Pilsbury

C_L7 *Stratus of bad weather*, or ragged Cumulus, or both, generally moving fast and changing shape rapidly. These clouds (known to mariners as 'scud') often form beneath a layer of Nimbostratus, as in the upper picture, or a layer of Altostratus, as in the lower picture.

69

C_L8 *Cumulus and Stratocumulus*, other than that formed from the spreading out of Cumulus, with their bases at different levels. The base of the Cumulus is normally at the lower level and occasionally the tops may reach or penetrate the Stratocumuli as shown in the lower picture.

70

C_L9 *Cumulonimbus with anvil.* This is a massive cloud of great vertical depth and horizontal extent, having a frayed-out fibrous top in the shape of an anvil. It normally develops from C_L3 and commonly gives rise to thunderstorms and/or hail showers. Underneath the base of the cloud, which is often very dark, there are frequent low, ragged clouds, which in storms are only a few hundred feet above the surface. Occasionally the upper parts of the cloud merge with Altostratus or Nimbostratus. The lower picture shows the appearance which the base of a Cumulonimbus cloud presents when it is overhead. The downward-hanging protuberances are due to turbulent downdraughts and are known as 'mamma'.

71

C$_M$1 *Thin Altostratus.*   The background cloud shown in both pictures has probably developed from thickening Cirrostratus associated with an approaching warm front. The upper picture shows a thin veil of cloud with a watery sun just visible. In the lower picture, the cloud has become a little thicker and obscures the sun. In both pictures there is still some stratocumulus below.

72

R.K. Pilsbury

R.K. Pilsbury

C$_M$2 *Thick Altostratus or Nimbostratus.* This develops from thickening C$_M$1. The upper picture shows a complete layer of cloud with Fractostratus, Pannus and 'scud' below and should be classified as Nimbostratus, whilst the lower picture shows Altostratus.

C$_M$3 *Semi-transparent Altocumulus*, at a single level, not invading the sky. The elements in the cloud sheet are small, rounded and more or less uniform; near the sun they are translucent. The sky may contain several Altocumulus patches of different opacity, as in the upper picture, or thin, lightly shaded sections, as in the lower picture.

74

R.K. Pilsbury

R.K. Pilsbury

C$_M$4 *Altocumulus lenticularis.*   The clouds shown in the picture are due to wave motion in the atmosphere and they are seen mainly over hilly country. At sea they are therefore likely to be seen only in certain coastal waters in the direction of the land. The cloud elements are smooth-looking and taper away towards the ends; they have bright translucent edges and show definite shading. In another variety of the cloud the elements are composed of fine granules and ripples lying in thin irregular patches, vaguely lenticular in shape and having fairly pronounced shading. Parts of the cloud near the sun often show the delicate colouring known as irisation, as seen in the lower picture.

C$_M$5 *Altocumulus increasing and thickening.* The essential feature of this cloud type is that it spreads from some particular direction on the horizon and increases in amount, perhaps finally covering the whole sky. It may be in one or more layers of varying degrees of density, some parts being translucent and others heavily shaded. Sometimes it may resemble Stratocumulus at a high level.

R.K. Pilsbury

R.K. Pilsbury

C$_M$6 *Altocumulus formed by the spreading out of Cumulus or Cumulonimbus.*   In certain atmospheric conditions, e.g. when there is a marked temperature inversion in the atmosphere which acts as a barrier to air rising by convection, the tops of these clouds reach a level above which they can rise no further, when they are compelled to flatten out horizontally, forming patches of Altocumulus of rather irregular thickness and shape, as shown in the upper picture. Care should be taken not to confuse these with the anvil-shaped tops of Cumulonimbus. If many large Cumulus-type clouds are present, the patches of Altocumulus, resulting from the spreading out of their tops, may coalesce to form quite an extensive layer. In the evening, convection dies down and the tops of large clouds will often spread out, as shown in the lower picture.

C_M7 *Altocumulus not increasing.*   This type includes:
    (a)   Patches, sheets or layers of Altocumulus at different levels, not increasing (upper picture);
    (b)   Patches, sheets or layers of Altocumulus at a single level, generally opaque, not increasing;
    (c)   Altocumulus, together with Altostratus or Nimbostratus (lower picture, with lines of Altocumulus in the distance but thin Altostratus overhead).

R.K. Pilsbury

R.K. Pilsbury

C$_M$8 *Altocumulus castellanus and Altocumulus floccus.*   Both these types are associated with developing thundery conditions over a wide area as opposed to thunderstorms arising from locally generated Cumulonimbus clouds. The upper picture shows long lines of Altocumulus castellanus silhouetted against the setting sun. The lower picture shows very ragged Altocumulus floccus in considerable quantity with one or two clouds showing castellated tops.

R.K. Pilsbury

R.K. Pilsbury

C_M9 *Altocumulus of a chaotic sky,* generally at several levels. The main characteristic of the sky is its heavy and stagnant appearance. There are usually clouds of all medium types mixed with clouds of type C_L and C_H. In the lower picture a few streaks of cloud, known as 'virga', can be seen in the lower middle distance.

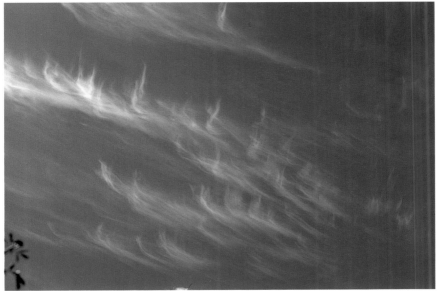

R.K. Pilsbury

R.K. Pilsbury

C$_H$1 *Cirrus in hooks or filaments*, not progressively invading the sky. The upper picture clearly shows the fibrous structure of Cirrus, with hooks at the ends of the fine strands. The lower picture shows fine strands of Cirrus with no hooks. These types of Cirrus often occur with other Cirrus clouds and should be classified as C$_H$1 only when the combined cover of all filaments, strands or hooks exceeds the total of other types of Cirrus present.

R.K. Pilsbury

R.K. Pilsbury

C$_H$2 *Dense Cirrus.* The Cirrus occurs in dense patches or entangled sheaves, upper picture, not usually increasing in amount. The two dense patches in the centre of the lower picture are typical examples. Sometimes the Cirrus is arranged in narrow bands, with sproutings in the shape of small turrets or battlements, or showing cumuliform tufts (lower picture).

C$_H$3 *Dense Cirrus from Cirrocumulus,* often in the form of an anvil. These clouds are white and fibrous and may be entirely separate from the Cumulonimbus of which they were a part.

83

C$_H$4 *Cirrus invading the sky.*   These clouds can be seen as separate, delicate filaments with fibrous trails. The Cirrus elements in the picture are moving from left to right, invading the sky and thickening, but no Cirrostratus is present.

R.K. Pilsbury

R.K. Pilsbury

C_H5 *Cirrus and/or Cirrostratus below 45° altitude.* A whitish veil progressively invading the sky but less than 45° above the horizon from which the cloud is spreading. Cirrus of this type develops as a result of the continued spread of C_H4. The clouds in the upper picture are Cirrus; in the lower picture, the Cirrus has merged into a sheet of Cirrostratus nearer the horizon.

R.K. Pilsbury

R.K. Pilsbury

C_H6 *Cirrus and/or Cirrostratus above 45° altitude.*   The pictures show Cirrus thickening rapidly to Cirrostratus, already extending higher than 45° above the horizon. The main sheet of Cirrostratus is often preceded by long filaments or hooks of Cirrus, sometimes in bands across the sky, as shown in the lower picture.

86

C$_H$7 *Veil of Cirrostratus covering the whole sky.* The cloud is usually light, uniform and nebulous, but it may be white and fibrous showing striations, as in the upper picture. It gives rise to halo phenomena around the sun or moon. Sometimes the veil is so thin that it is difficult to distinguish it from the blue sky, and halo phenomena may provide the only reliable evidence of its presence.

R.K. Pilsbury

R.K. Pilsbury

C$_H$8 *Cirrostratus not increasing and not covering the whole sky.* The veil or sheet of clouds extends from one horizon but leaves a segment of blue sky in the other direction. The cloud either remains constant in amount or decreases. The upper picture shows a fairly dense sheet of Cirrostratus clearing away after the passage of a cold front.

R.K. Pilsbury

R.K. Pilsbury

C_H9 *Cirrocumulus.* This code figure is only used when the amount of Cirrocumulus is greater than any other types of Cirrus which may be present. The upper picture shows a typical example, the cloud elements being very much smaller than those found in Altocumulus. In the lower picture, the elements are composed of small, ragged cumuliform tufts.

I.C. Ligertwood

E.D. Somes

Two examples of 'Roll Cumulus' cloud, Stratocumulus stratiformis.

Orographic cloud over Table Mountain, Cape Town.

Altocumulus lenticularis over Lion's Head, Cape Peninsula.

C.P. Row

Stratocumulus in parallel layers over St Michael's Mount, Cornwall.

J.A. Walton

Noctilucent cloud. Clouds at a height of 80 km or higher, often with a bluish or silvery tinge or occasionally red or orange in colour. They are only visible at night, in the northern sky, an hour or more after sunset or before sunrise around mid-summer in the northern hemisphere or mid-winter in the southern hemisphere. (See page 160.)

Crown copyright

Crown copyright

Two examples of crepuscular rays at twilight, appearing from behind cumulus and cumulonimbus clouds. (See page 165)

93

CHAPTER 6

OCEAN WAVES

The complex nature of wave motion at sea
The action of wind in producing waves is not precisely understood. The effect of the wind varies from the tiny ripples ruffled on a pond by the merest breath of air to the mighty rollers of the North Atlantic and Roaring Forties. All ocean waves, other than those caused by movements of the sea floor and tidal effects, owe their origin to the generating action of the wind. Wave motion, however, may persist even after the generating force has disappeared, being then slowly dissipated by frictional forces.

An observer of the motion of the sea surface at a particular place will, in general, notice a complicated wave form such as is shown in Figure 23 (page 98), which may be regarded as the result of the superposition of a number of simple regular wave motions having different lengths and speeds.

The ideal observer is an instrument known as a wave-recorder which registers automatically the up and down motion of the water surface and enables a record such as Figure 20 to be drawn. This record can be analysed or split up into its component simple waves. Most wave-recorders can only be effectively used from the shore, offshore installations or from stationary ships and hence it is not possible to measure sea disturbance in general by this method although it would be most desirable to do so.

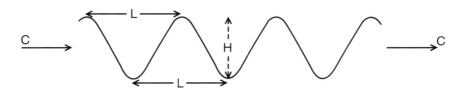

Figure 20.   Characteristics of a simple wave.

The distinction between sea and swell
The system of waves raised by the local wind blowing at the time of observation is usually referred to as 'sea'. Those waves not raised by the local wind blowing at the time of observation, but due either to winds blowing at a distance or to winds that have ceased to blow, are known collectively as 'swell'. Usually, one component of the swell dominates the rest, but occasionally two component wave motions crossing at an angle may be observed. These are referred to as 'cross swells'. Sea and swell may both be present at the same time and the sea may be from a different direction and have different period and height to the swell, or both sea and swell may be from the same direction.

The characteristics of a simple wave

The following definitions are used in describing a simple wave:

(a) SPEED, C, usually expressed in knots, is the speed at which individual waves travel.

(b) LENGTH, L, expressed in metres, is the horizontal distance between successive crests or successive troughs.

(c) PERIOD, T, expressed in seconds, is the time interval required for the passage of successive crests (or successive troughs) past a given point.

(d) HEIGHT, H, expressed in metres, is the vertical distance between the top of a crest and the bottom of a trough.

The following relations are found to hold for a simple wave:

Speed $= 3.1 \times$ period
Length $= 1.555 \times (\text{period})^2$ metres.

(In application to actual sea waves, which are not simple, the constant 1.555 should be reduced by a factor ranging between about 1/2 and 1/3.)

By means of these formulae, measurements of one of the variables can be used to calculate the other two. The following table gives these relations numerically for different wave periods:

Period seconds	Length Metres	Speed Knots
2	6.2	6.2
4	24.9	12.4
6	56.0	18.6
8	99.5	24.8
10	155.5	31.0
12	223.9	37.2
14	304.8	43.4
16	398.0	49.6
18	503.9	55.8
20	622.0	62.0

There is no inherent theoretical relation between the height and period of a simple wave. We can imagine the height to be varied at will, the period (and hence length and speed) remaining constant. In real wave motion, however, in which many simple waves are superposed there is a further consideration that enables us to see how the height is limited. If we call the quotient H/L the 'steepness' of the wave, it is found that the mean steepness does not increase beyond 7.6 per cent (1/13). If the mean steepness is less than this figure then the waves are capable of absorbing more energy from the wind, thus increasing their height relative to their length. When the limiting steepness is reached, surplus energy received from the wind is dissipated by the breaking of the waves at the crests (white horses). This limiting value of the steepness explains why the mean maximum height of the sea waves is roughly in proportion to their length; for example, wind-driven waves of length 120 m (period 9 seconds) would not be expected to have a mean maximum height greater than 9 m. If the wavelength were about 150 m (period 10 seconds) this limiting value of the mean maximum height would be increased to 12 m. On the other hand, long swells, perhaps 300–600 m in length, may have heights of less than half a metre.

When the height of the wave is small compared with its length, the wave profile can be adequately represented by a simple sine curve. As the height becomes relatively greater, however, it is seen that the crests become sharper and the troughs much more rounded, the precise profile being a curve known as a 'trochoid'. This is the curve that would be traced on a bulkhead by a marking point fixed to the spoke of a wheel, if we imagined the wheel to be rolled along under the deckhead.

In Figure 21 the large circle represents the wheel and P the marking point on a spoke, OP, the distance from the axle being called the tracing arm. The arrow shows the direction in which the circle rolls and in which the wave is supposed to be travelling. AB is the base, i.e. the straight line under which the circle is to roll, the length AB being equal to the half circumference of the wheel, AR.

Now as the circle rolls, when position 3 of the circle reaches position 3 of the base, the semicircle FPG will be in the position shown by the dotted semicircle; and the marking point P will coincide with the point D, having described part of a trochoid PD. When the circle has completed half a revolution, the marking point P will coincide with E, having described the trochoid curve PDE which is half a wavelength; the diameter POH represents the height of the wave. The nearer the marking point is to the axle of the wheel, the flatter will be the trochoid.

In an ideal wave each water particle revolves with uniform speed in a circular orbit, perpendicular to the wave ridge (the diameter of the orbital circles being the height of the wave) and completes a revolution in the same time as the wave takes to advance its own length. At a wave crest the motion of the particles is wholly horizontal, advancing in the same direction as the wave; at mid height on the front slope it is wholly upwards; in the trough it is again horizontal but in the opposite direction to the travel of the wave, and at mid height on the back slope it is wholly downwards. This motion may be seen by watching a floating object at the passage of a wave. The object describes a circle but is not carried bodily forward by the wave.

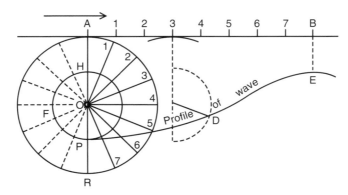

Figure 21.   Representation of a trochoidal wave form.

The disturbance set up by wave motion must necessarily extend for some distance below the surface; but its magnitude decreases very rapidly in accordance with a definite law, the trochoids becoming flatter and flatter as the depth increases, and the water particles revolving in ever-decreasing circles. At a depth of one wavelength the disturbance is less than a five-hundredth part of what is at the surface, so that the water at that depth may be considered undisturbed. The motion associated with the largest ocean waves is inappreciable at even moderate depths, as is demonstrated by experience in submarines.

Wave groups
Experience shows that waves generally travel in groups with patches of dead water in between, the wave height being a maximum at the centre of each group. We have said earlier that any observed wave motion can be regarded as built up from a number of simple wave forms. Let us consider, for example, the superposition of two simple wave motions having the same height but slightly different periods. If the crests of the two wave motions are made to coincide at the initial point of observation the height of the resultant wave will be twice that of each component wave. To each side of this point, however, owing to the difference of period, the additive effect becomes less until a point is reached where the heights of the component waves, being of different sign, completely annul each other's effect. Beyond this point the heights again become additive until the troughs of component waves coincide. In other words, there is a variation of height superposed on the ordinary wave motion. It can also be shown that two simple wave trains moving in slightly different directions give a resultant pattern composed of 'short-crested' waves as distinct from the 'long-crested' waves of simple wave motions.

The speed of a wave group is not the same as that of the individual waves composing it. Each individual wave in its turn emerges from the dead water in the rear of the group, travels through the group and subsides in the dead water ahead of it. The speed of the wave group must therefore be less than the speed of an individual wave. Both theoretical considerations and experience show that the wave group travels at one half the speed of the individual waves.

The origin and travel of swell
Swell waves originate in the heavy seas created in a storm area. Short waves have an insufficient store of energy to enable them to travel long distances against the dissipating action of friction. Hence, in general, it follows that swell waves are long waves in comparison with the wind driven waves at the place of observation.

In calculating the distance travelled by swell, care must be taken to distinguish between the speed of the individual waves and the speed of the wave groups. If, for example, a ship reports the sudden onset of waves whose speed, calculated from the period, is 30 knots, then another ship in the line of advance of these waves will experience their onset at a time obtained by allowing a speed of $\frac{1}{2} \times 30 = 15$ knots for the disturbance.

As swell travels its height decreases. Investigations by the Institute of Oceanographic Sciences Deacon Laboratory show that if R is the distance from the point of generation in nautical miles then the amplitude of distance R is $(300/R)^{1/2}$ of that at the point of generation by the wind. Thus, a swell would lose one-half of its height in travelling a distance of 1200 nautical miles. The long swells are the greatest travellers.

Waves in shallow water

All the previous remarks refer to waves in deep water. When a deep-water wave enters shallow waters it undergoes profound modification. Its speed is reduced, its direction of motion may be changed and, finally, its height increases until, on reaching a certain limiting depth, the wave breaks on the shore. Water may be regarded as shallow when the depth is less than half the length of the wave.

The decrease in speed when a wave approaches the shore accounts for the fact that the wave fronts become, in general, parallel to the shore prior to breaking. Figure 22 shows a wave, approaching the shore at an angle, being refracted until it becomes parallel to the shore.

The same reasoning may be applied to explain how waves are able to bend round headlands and to progress into sheltered bays.

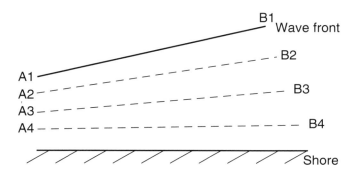

Figure 22.   Refraction of a wave approaching the shore at an angle.

OBSERVING OCEAN WAVES

The inherent difficulties of observation

It has been mentioned earlier that the ideal observer is a wave-recorder which can register automatically the up and down motion of the sea surface at a fixed point. A typical record is shown in Figure 23.

The record is, in general, complex and shows immediately all the difficulties inherent in eye observation. For example, are all the waves to be considered on an equal footing or are only the big waves to be counted? Since the wave

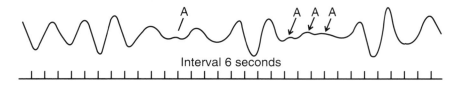

Figure 23.   Wave form of the sea surface.

98

characteristics vary so much, what average values shall be taken? It is obvious that if comparable results are to be obtained the observer must follow a definite procedure. The flat and badly formed waves ('A' in Figure 23) between the wave groups cannot be observed accurately by eye and different observers would undoubtedly get different results if an attempt were made to include them in the record. The method to be adopted, therefore, is to observe only the well-formed waves in the centre of the wave groups. The observation of waves entails the measurement or estimation of the following characteristics:

Direction   Period   Height.

Reliable average values of period and height can only be obtained by observing at least twenty waves. Of course, these cannot be consecutive; a few must be selected from each succeeding wave group until the required number has been obtained. Only measurements or quite good estimates are required. Rough guesses have little value and should not be recorded.

It will often be found that there are waves coming from more than one direction. For example, there may be a sea caused by the wind then blowing and a swell caused by a wind that has either passed over or is blowing in a distant area. Or there may be two swells (i.e. cross swells) caused by winds blowing from different directions in distant areas. In such cases the observer should distinguish between sea and swell, and report them separately, giving two groups for swell when appropriate.

The direction, height and period of the sea wave may be quite different from that of the swell wave. It will, however, often happen — particularly with winds of Beaufort force 8 and above — that the sea and swell waves are both coming from the same direction. In that case it is virtually impossible to differentiate between sea and swell and the best answer is to look upon the combined wave as being a sea wave and log it accordingly.

Observing waves from a moving ship
Care must be taken to ensure that the observations, especially those of period, are not influenced by the waves generated by the motion of the ship.

(a) *Direction from which the waves come.* This is easily obtained either by sighting directly across the wave front or by sighting along the crests of the waves and remembering that the required direction differs from this by 90 degrees.

(b) *Period.* For measurements of period a stopwatch is desirable. If this is not available an ordinary watch with a seconds hand may be used or, alternatively, a practised observer may count seconds.

The observer selects a distinctive patch of foam or a small object floating on the water at some distance from the ship, and notes the time at which it is on the crest of each successive wave. The procedure is repeated for the larger waves of each successive group until at least twenty observations are available. The period is then taken as the average time for a complete oscillation from crest to crest. In a fast ship it will be found that the 'patch of foam' method will rarely last for more than one complete oscillation and that many waves have to be observed separately. With practice, suitable waves can easily be picked out and the timing from crest to crest becomes quite simple. When it is desired to use a suitably buoyant and biodegradable object, it should be thrown into the sea as far forward as possible.

Another method available to the observer with a stopwatch is to observe two or more consecutive 'central' waves of a wave group while the watch is running continuously, then to stop the watch until the central waves of the next wave group appear, the watch being then restarted. This procedure is repeated until at least twenty complete oscillations have been observed. The period is then obtained by dividing the total time by the number of oscillations. It is important to note that the periods between times of crests passing a point on the ship are not the ones required.

(c) *Height.*   Although wave-recorders are fitted to some research ships and marine automatic weather stations, there is at present no method of measuring the height of waves suitable for general use on merchant ships, but a practised observer can make useful estimates. The procedure to be adopted depends on the length of the waves relative to the length of the ship. If the length of the waves is short in comparison with the ship's length, i.e. if the ship spans two or more wave crests, the height should be estimated from the appearance of the waves at or on the side of the ship, at times when the pitching and rolling of the ship is least. For the best result the observer should take up a position as low down the ship as possible, preferably amidships where the effect of pitching is least, and on the side of the ship towards which the waves are coming.

This method fails when the length of the waves exceeds the length of the ship, for then the ship rises bodily with the passage of each wave crest. The observer should then take up a position in the ship so that his eye is just in line with the advancing wave crest and the horizon, when the ship is upright in the trough. The height of eye above the ship's water line is then the height of the wave. The nearer the observer is to an amidships position the less chance will there be of the measurement being vitiated by pitching. If the ship rolls heavily it is particularly important to make the observation at the moment when she is upright in the trough. Exaggeration of estimates of wave height is mostly due to errors caused by rolling. (See Figure 24. When the ship is rolling (b), the observer at 'O' has to take up a higher position to get a line on the horizon than when she is upright (a).)

(a)

(b)

Figure 24.   Estimation of wave height at sea.

The observation of height of waves is most difficult when the length of the waves exceeds the length of the ship and their height is small. The best estimate of height can be obtained by going as near the water as possible, but even then the observation can only be rough. In making height estimates an attempt should be made to fix a standard of height in terms of the height of a man or the height of a bulwark, forecastle or well-known dimension in the ship. There is generally a tendency to overestimate the height of long waves.

Estimating the height of a wave from a high bridge in a fast ship is a difficult job and much will depend on the skill and ingenuity of the observer; in many cases all one can hope for is a very rough estimate.

All estimates of wave height should be made preferably with the ship on an even keel so that the observer's height of eye is consistent.

The inherent difficulties already mentioned, together with the practical difficulties of estimation, make it essential that the recorded height should be the average value of about twenty distinct observations. These observations should be made on the central waves of the more prominent wave groups.

Wave observations at night or in low visibility

Under these conditions the most that the observer can normally hope to record is direction and an estimate of height, or perhaps direction only, which would at least indicate the presence of waves. Such observations might be of considerable value in tropical waters in the hurricane season. It is only on very bright nights that the observations of period would be practicable.

Observing waves from weather ships

Wave-recorders, which can record the period and height of the waves, have been installed in most ocean weather ships. But even when no special instruments are carried, weather ships have the advantage of being able to manoeuvre so as to secure the best conditions for wave observation. The methods outlined in (b) may be used to better advantage than by ordinary merchant ships. For example, a floating object may be observed for a considerable time; it is not lost in the distance as occurs when the ship is moving.

In addition to these observations the height, length and period of waves can be determined from a stationary ship as follows:

(a) The estimation of wave height may be much assisted with the use of a dan buoy of known height.

(b) Length can be observed by streaming a buoy for such a distance astern that the crests of successive waves are simultaneously passing the buoy and the observer. This distance between the two is the wavelength.

(c) Period can be obtained by noting the time taken for the wave to travel the distance between the buoy and the observer.

By simple division the speed of the individual waves can be deduced.

The importance of wave observations

The study of ocean waves has only recently been put on a scientific basis by the utilization of an automatic method of recording and the subsequent analysis of the record into component simple waves. The establishment of a network of specially equipped observing stations would probably add much to our present knowledge of the generation, transmission and decay of ocean waves. The new method of recording has made evident the limitations of former methods of observation, including the use of sea and swell scales, and has indicated the necessity of obtaining quantitative observations of wave characteristics.

Of practical importance is the fact that quantitative wave observations may be used for identifying the approximate position of a storm centre when suitable weather observations are lacking. The use of swell as an indication of the approach of a tropical storm is well known. The forecasting of swell on exposed coasts, such as those of Morocco and Portugal, is of considerable value for the protection of coastal shipping and port installations. The accuracy of these forecasts depends largely on an adequate supply of reliable ships' observations. Statistics of the period and height of waves would be of value to naval architects particularly in respect of stability, rolling and behaviour of the ship structure in a seaway.

CHAPTER 7

OBSERVATIONS OF OCEAN CURRENTS AND ICE

OCEAN CURRENT OBSERVATIONS

Introduction
Present knowledge of the general patterns of surface currents of the oceans has been largely derived from the systematically recorded observations made from ships on passage over more than a century. This knowledge is summarized in atlases, charts and Sailing Directions which have been prepared for the benefit of the navigator. However, much remains to be learnt about the currents, for instance about the general flow of waters that are remote from the main shipping routes, about local variations and intensities of currents and about the variabilities of currents through the course of the year and from one year to another. Consequently there is a continuing need for observations of surface currents. Moreover, as improved navigational aids allow increasing accuracy and frequency of observation, better and more-detailed analyses of the currents will become possible, to the benefit not only of navigation but also of the various aspects of marine science.

Marine observers are reminded that towards the end of the *Meteorological Logbook* is a section reserved for recording the set and drift of currents observed during a voyage. Observations of ocean currents will be very welcome from any ship, whether reporting meteorological observations or not.

The method of observing currents. This consists of deriving the set and drift from the direction and distance respectively between a dead-reckoning (DR) position (obtained making due allowance for leeway) and the corresponding observed position. The current so deduced is the mean current affecting the ship over the distance between the fixes when the DR plot was started (the 'From' position) and finished (the 'To' position); it is assumed that this is the current at a depth of about half the ship's draught.

In calculating the DR position it is important that the course or courses should be corrected for leeway so that — as far as can be judged — the difference between DR and 'To' positions is due only to current and not to a combination of wind and current. The assessment of leeway can only be made by the mariner with his full knowledge of the vessel's performance and state of loading. If he has considerable doubt about the appropriate allowance for leeway — say because of gales during the period of the DR plot — an observation should not be recorded.

In general, observations should not be recorded when the derived value of current is likely to be unrepresentative or inaccurate. The following aspects concerning the representativeness and accuracy of observation should be borne in mind.

Representativeness of observations. The ideal observation of current would represent the purely non-tidal movement of water at a single point at a given time. Such an observation cannot be made in practice from a ship on passage but the departure from the ideal does not usually decrease the value of the results to a serious extent so long as certain limitations are heeded. An observation of current should not be made:

(a) where significant tidal streams are to be expected;

(b) when the distance between 'From' and 'To' positions exceeds about 400 miles;

(c) when the 'From' and 'To' positions are separated by more than a day's sailing — say by more than 25 hours, allowing for the ship's clocks being retarded;

(d) when there is reason to believe that the current changes significantly between the 'From' and 'To' positions, i.e. when passing from one system of currents to another, when passing a strait, a cape, or a current race;

(e) so as to overlap another observation: for example if there are successive fixes at positions A, B, C and D the overlapping observations from A to C and from B to D are both required since they are not independent of each other; and

(f) when the accuracy of either the 'From' or 'To' fix is suspect.

Accuracy of observations. In effect the observed current is calculated from the difference between two vectors, i.e. the vector representing movement of the ship with respect to the water and the vector representing movement over the ocean bed. Since the difference is normally much smaller than either vector, the accuracies of values used to calculate these vectors crucially affect the accuracy of the inferred current.

The vector of movement with respect to the water depends on course (corrected for leeway) and on distance run through the water. Distance run can be measured with high accuracy by means of satellite navigation equipment. If it is necessary to assess distance run from propeller revolutions the allowance for slip under the prevailing conditions (wind, sea, draught, state of ship's bottom) becomes important.

The accuracy of the vector of movement over the ocean bed is governed by the accuracy of the two fixes — for the 'From' and 'To' positions. Usually accurate fixes may also be derived by a number of means, such as by observations of two or more stars at twilight, or by LORAN or Omega navigational systems. A noon position based on forenoon sight and meridian altitude is not desirable for calculation of current if more-accurate types of fix are available since the run between sights depends on a due appreciation of the current — the very element that is being sought.

Interval between 'From' and 'To' positions. As already stated the interval should not be too large; if the ship passes through two or more different currents then the observed (mean) value will be representative of none of the constituent currents. On the other hand the interval should not be too small since a given error in position fixing will produce an error in the calculated rate of current which is greater if the interval of time is shorter than if it is long. The combination of a possibly inaccurate fix and short interval of time would make unreliable, for example, an observation based on a noon position, found from forenoon sight and meridian altitude, and a fix at approximately 1415, using the Sun and Venus. Indeed, whenever use is made of a noon position based on forenoon and noon sights — with its inherent inaccuracies, however carefully compiled — the current should be calculated over the longest permissible interval of about 24 hours. At the other extreme, with both fixes highly accurate (say by satellite) an interval as short as three hours might be adequate.

ICE OBSERVATIONS

Under the International Convention for the Safety of Life at Sea, 1974, the Master of every ship that meets with dangerous ice has the obligation to report this by all means available to ships in the vicinity and to the nearest coast radio station or signal station. (Details of the prescribed form of signal are given in Chapter 14.)

Apart from this primary obligation with regard to the immediate safety of life, the mariner provides important contributions to the knowledge of ice at sea, by including in the routine synoptic weather report an ICE group or a plain-language report of ice whenever this is appropriate. This information is used especially for mapping the existing state and development of the ice as a basis for operational advice to mariners.

Some background knowledge of the physics and climatology of sea ice and icebergs is helpful to the observer. Such knowledge can be obtained from *Meteorology for Mariners* — Chapter 17 deals with formation and movement and Chapter 18 with distribution of sea ice and icebergs. Also the latest edition of *The Mariner's Handbook*, NP 100, published by the Hydrographic Office, contains a chapter on ice and gives a selection of photographs illustrating a number of ice terms. Some of these photographs are shown between pages 117 and 140.

To ensure consistency in the use of terms for ice these have been defined by the World Meteorological Organization (WMO) and published in a glossary entitled *WMO Sea-ice Nomenclature*; the publication is comprehensively illustrated by photographs.

The terms of the *Nomenclature* with full definitions, incorporating the latest amendments and arranged in alphabetical order, are reproduced on the following pages. To assist the observer in selecting the term most appropriate for a certain state or process this alphabetical list is preceded by a section in which terms are arranged according to subject. Some brief explanatory remarks are included in this section but reference should be made to the alphabetical list for the full definition of any term.

ICE TERMS ARRANGED BY SUBJECT

1. *FLOATING ICE*
    Any form of ice found floating in water. The principal kinds of floating ice are lake ice, river ice and sea ice which form by the freezing of water at the surface, and glacier ice (ice of land origin) formed on land or in an ice shelf. The concept includes ice that is stranded or grounded.

1.1   **Sea ice:**   Any form of ice found at sea which has originated from the freezing of sea water.

1.1.1   *FAST ICE:*   cf. 3.1

1.1.2   *DRIFT ICE/PACK ICE:*   Term used in a wide sense to include any area of sea ice other than fast ice no matter what form it takes or how it is disposed. When concentrations are high, i.e. 7/10 or more, drift ice may be replaced by the term pack ice*.

*Previously the term pack ice was used for all ranges of concentration.

1.2   **Ice of land origin:**   Ice formed on land or in an ice shelf, found floating in water. The concept includes ice that is stranded or grounded.

1.3   **Lake ice:**   Ice formed on a lake, regardless of observed location.

1.4   **River ice:**   Ice formed on a river, regardless of observed location.

2. DEVELOPMENT

2.1   **New ice:**   A general term for recently formed ice which includes frazil ice, grease ice, slush and shuga. These types of ice are composed of ice crystals which are only weakly frozen together (if at all) and have a definite form only while they are afloat.

2.1.1   *FRAZIL ICE:*   Fine spicules or plates of ice, suspended in water.

2.1.2   *GREASE ICE:*   A later stage of freezing than frazil ice when the crystals have coagulated to form a soupy layer on the surface. Grease ice reflects little light, giving the sea a matt appearance.

2.1.3   *SLUSH:*   Snow which is saturated and mixed with water on land or ice surfaces, or as a viscous floating mass in water after a heavy snowfall.

2.1.4   *SHUGA:*   An accumulation of spongy white ice lumps, a few centimetres across; they are formed from grease ice or slush and sometimes from anchor ice rising to the surface.

2.2   **Nilas:**   A thin elastic crust of ice, easily bending on waves and swell and under pressure, thrusting in a pattern of interlocking 'fingers' (finger rafting). Has a matt surface and is up to 10 cm in thickness. May be subdivided into dark nilas and light nilas.

2.2.1   *DARK NILAS:*   Nilas which is under 5 cm in thickness and is very dark in colour.

2.2.2   *LIGHT NILAS:*   Nilas which is more than 5 cm in thickness and rather lighter in colour than dark nilas.

2.2.3   *ICE RIND:*   A brittle shiny crust of ice formed on a quiet surface by direct freezing or from grease ice, usually in water of low salinity. Thickness to about 5 cm. Easily broken by wind or swell, commonly breaking in rectangular pieces.

2.3   **Pancake ice:**   cf. 4.3.1.

2.4   **Young ice:**   Ice in the transition stage between nilas and first-year ice, 10–30 cm in thickness. May be subdivided into grey ice and grey-white ice.

2.4.1   *GREY ICE:*   Young ice 10–15 cm thick. Less elastic than nilas and breaks on swell. Usually rafts under pressure.

2.4.2   *GREY-WHITE ICE:*   Young ice 15–30 cm thick. Under pressure more likely to ridge than raft.

2.5   **First-year ice:**   Sea ice of not more than one winter's growth, developing from young ice; thickness 30 cm–2 m. May be subdivided into thin first-year ice/white ice, medium first-year ice and thick first-year ice.

2.5.1   *THIN FIRST-YEAR ICE/WHITE ICE:*   First-year ice 30–70 cm thick.

2.5.1.1   *Thin first-year ice/white ice first stage:*   30–50 cm thick.

2.5.1.2   *Thin first-year ice/white ice second stage:*   50–70 cm thick.

2.5.2   *MEDIUM FIRST-YEAR ICE:*   First-year ice 70–120 cm thick.

2.5.3   *THICK FIRST-YEAR ICE:*   First-year ice over 120 cm thick.

2.6   **Old ice:**   Sea ice which has survived at least one summer's melt; typical thickness up to 3 m or more. Most topographic features are smoother than on first-year ice. May be subdivided into second-year ice and multi-year ice.

2.6.1   *SECOND-YEAR ICE:*   Old ice which has survived only one summer's melt; typical thickness up to 2.5 m and sometimes more. Because it is thicker than first-year ice, it stands higher out of the water. In contrast to multi-year ice, summer melting produces a regular pattern of numerous small puddles. Bare patches and puddles are usually greenish-blue.

2.6.2   *MULTI-YEAR ICE:*   Old ice up to 3 m or more thick which has survived at least two summers' melt. Hummocks even smoother than in second-year ice, and the ice is almost salt-free. Colour, where bare, is usually blue. Melt pattern consists of large interconnecting irregular puddles and a well-developed drainage system.

3.   *FORMS OF FAST ICE*

3.1   **Fast ice:**   Sea ice which forms and remains fast along the coast, where it is attached to the shore, to an ice wall, to an ice front, between shoals or grounded icebergs. Vertical fluctuations may be observed during changes of sea level. Fast ice may be formed in situ from sea water or by freezing of floating ice of any age to the shore and it may extend a few metres or several hundred kilometres from the coast. Fast ice may be more than one year old and may then be prefixed with the appropriate age category (old, second-year, or multi-year). If it is thicker than about 2 m above sea level it is called an ice shelf.

3.1.1   *YOUNG COASTAL ICE:*   The initial stage of fast ice formation consisting of nilas or young ice, its width varying from a few metres up to 100–200 m from the shoreline.

3.2   **Icefoot:**   A narrow fringe of ice attached to the coast, unmoved by tides and remaining after the fast ice has moved away.

3.3   **Anchor ice:**   Submerged ice attached or anchored to the bottom, irrespective of the nature of its formation.

3.4   **Grounded ice:**   Floating ice which is aground in shoal water (cf. stranded ice).

3.4.1   *STRANDED ICE:*   Ice which has been floating and has been deposited on the shore by retreating high water.

3.4.2   *GROUNDED HUMMOCK:*   Hummocked grounded ice formation. There are single grounded hummocks and lines (or chains) of grounded hummocks.

4.   *OCCURRENCE OF FLOATING ICE*

4.1   **Ice cover:**   The ratio of an area of ice of any concentration to the total area of sea surface within some large geographic locale; this locale may be global, hemispheric, or prescribed by a specific oceanographic entity such as Baffin Bay or the Barents Sea.

4.2   **Concentration:**   The ratio expressed in tenths* describing the amount of the sea surface covered by ice as a fraction of the whole area being considered. Total concentration includes all stages of development that are present; partial concentration may refer to the amount of a particular stage or of a particular form of ice and represents only a part of the total.

4.2.1   *COMPACT ICE:*   Floating ice in which the concentration is $^{10}/_{10}$ and no water is visible.

4.2.1.1   *Consolidated ice:*   Floating ice in which the concentration is $^{10}/_{10}$ and the floes are frozen together.

4.2.2   *VERY CLOSE ICE:*   Floating ice in which the concentration is $^{9}/_{10}$ to less than $^{10}/_{10}$.

4.2.3   *CLOSE ICE:*   Floating ice in which the concentration is $^{7}/_{10}$ to $^{8}/_{10}$, composed of floes mostly in contact.

4.2.4   *OPEN ICE:*   Floating ice in which the ice concentration is $^{4}/_{10}$ to $^{6}/_{10}$, with many leads and polynyas, and the floes are generally not in contact with one another.

4.2.5   *VERY OPEN ICE:*   Floating ice in which the concentration is $^{1}/_{10}$ to $^{3}/_{10}$ and water preponderates over ice.

4.2.6   *OPEN WATER:*   A large area of freely navigable water in which sea ice is present in concentrations less than $^{1}/_{10}$. No ice of land origin is present.

4.2.7   *BERGY WATER:*   An area of freely navigable water in which ice of land origin is present in concentrations less than $^{1}/_{10}$. There may be sea ice present, although the total concentration of all ice shall not exceed $^{1}/_{10}$.

4.2.8   *ICE-FREE:*   No ice present. If ice of any kind is present this term should not be used.

4.3   **Forms of floating ice**

4.3.1   *PANCAKE ICE:*   Predominantly circular pieces of ice from 30 cm–3 m in diameter, and up to about 10 cm in thickness, with raised rims due to the pieces striking against one another. It may be formed on a slight swell from grease ice, shuga or slush or as a result of the breaking of ice rind, nilas or, under severe conditions of swell or waves, of grey ice. It also sometimes forms at some depth, at an interface between water bodies of different physical characteristics, from where it floats to the surface; its appearance may rapidly cover wide areas of water.

*In historical sea-ice data oktas have been used by some countries.

| 4.3.2 | *FLOE:*   Any relatively flat piece of sea ice 20 m or more across. Floes are subdivided according to horizontal extent as follows: |

4.3.2   *FLOE:*   Any relatively flat piece of sea ice 20 m or more across. Floes are subdivided according to horizontal extent as follows:

4.3.2.1   *Giant:*   Over 10 km across.

4.3.2.2   *Vast:*   2–10 km across.

4.3.2.3   *Big:*   500–2000 m across.

4.3.2.4   *Medium:*   100–500 m across.

4.3.2.5   *Small:*   20–100 m across.

4.3.3   *ICE CAKE:*   Any relatively flat piece of sea ice less than 20 m across.

4.3.3.1   *Small ice cake:*   An ice cake less than 2 m across.

4.3.4   *FLOEBERG:*   A massive piece of sea ice composed of a hummock, or a group of hummocks frozen together, and separated from any ice surroundings. It may typically protrude up to 5 m above sea-level.

4.3.4.1   *Floebit:*   A relatively small piece of sea ice, normally not more than 10 m across composed of hummocks or parts of ridges frozen together and separated from any surroundings. It typically protrudes up to 2 m above sea-level.

4.3.5   *ICE BRECCIA:*   Ice of different stages of development frozen together.

4.3.6   *BRASH ICE:*   Accumulations of floating ice made up of fragments not more than 2 m across, the wreckage of other forms of ice.

4.3.7   *ICEBERG:*   cf. 10.4.2.

4.3.8   *GLACIER BERG:*   cf. 10.4.2.1.

4.3.9   *TABULAR BERG:*   cf. 10.4.2.2.

4.3.10   *ICE ISLAND:*   cf. 10.4.3.

4.3.11   *BERGY BIT:*   cf. 10.4.4

4.3.12   *GROWLER:*   cf. 10.4.5

4.4   **Arrangement**

4.4.1   *ICE FIELD:*   Area of floating ice consisting of any size of floes, which is greater than 10 km across (cf. patch).

4.4.1.1   *Large ice field:*   An ice field over 20 km across.

4.4.1.2   *Medium ice field:*   An ice field 15–20 km across.

4.4.1.3   *Small ice field:*   An ice field 10–15 km across.

4.4.1.4   *Ice patch:*   An area of floating ice less than 10 km across.

4.4.2   *ICE MASSIF:*   A variable accumulation of close or very close ice covering hundreds of square kilometres which is found in the same region every summer.

4.4.3   *BELT:*   A large feature of drift ice arrangement, longer than it is wide, from 1 km to more than 100 km in width.

4.4.4   *TONGUE:*   A projection of the ice edge up to several kilometres in length, caused by wind or current.

4.4.5   *STRIP:*   Long narrow area of floating ice, about 1 km or less in width, usually composed of small fragments detached from the main mass of ice, and run together under the influence of wind, swell or current.

4.4.5.1   *Ice isthmus:*   A narrow connection between two ice areas of very close or compact ice. It may be difficult to pass, whilst sometimes being part of a recommended route.

4.4.6   *BIGHT:*   An extensive crescent-shaped indentation in the ice edge, formed by either wind or current.

4.4.7   *ICE JAM:*   An accumulation of broken river ice or sea ice caught in a narrow channel.

4.4.8   *ICE EDGE:*   The demarcation at any given time between the open sea and sea ice of any kind, whether fast or drifting. It may be termed compacted or diffuse (cf. ice boundary).

4.4.8.1   *Compacted ice edge:*   Close, clear-cut ice edge, compacted by wind or current; usually on the windward side of an area of drift ice.

4.4.8.1.1   Jammed brash barrier: A strip or narrow belt of new, young or brash ice (usually 100–5000 m wide) formed at the edge of either drift or fast ice or at the shore. It is heavily compacted mostly due to wind action and may extend 2 to 20 m below the surface but does not normally have appreciable topography. Jammed brash barriers may disperse with changing winds but can also consolidate to form a strip of unusually thick ice in comparison with the surrounding drift ice.

4.4.8.2   *Diffuse ice edge:*   Poorly defined ice edge limiting an area of dispersed ice; usually on the leeward side of an area of drift ice.

4.4.8.3   *Ice limit:*   Climatological term referring to the extreme minimum or extreme maximum extent of the ice edge in any given month or period based on observations over a number of years. Term should be preceded by minimum or maximum (cf. mean ice edge).

4.4.8.4   *Mean ice edge:*   Average position of the ice edge in any given month or period based on observations over a number of years. Other terms which may be used are mean maximum ice edge and mean minimum ice edge (cf. ice limit).

4.4.8.5   *Fast-ice edge:*   The demarcation at any given time between fast ice and open water.

4.4.9   *ICE BOUNDARY:*   The demarcation at any given time between fast ice and drift ice or between areas of drift ice of different concentrations (cf. ice edge).

4.4.9.1   *Fast-ice boundary:*   The ice boundary at any given time between fast ice and drift ice.

4.4.9.2   *Concentration boundary:*   A line approximating the transition between two areas of drift ice with distinctly different concentrations.

4.4.10   *ICEBERG TONGUE:*   cf. 10.4.2.3.

5.   *FLOATING ICE MOTION PROCESSES*

5.1   **Diverging:**   Ice fields or floes in an area are subjected to diverging or dispersive motion, thus reducing ice concentration and/or relieving stresses in the ice.

5.2   **Compacting:**   Pieces of floating ice are said to be compacting when they are subjected to a converging motion, which increases ice concentration and/or produces stresses which may result in ice deformation.

5.3   **Shearing:**   An area of drift ice is subject to shear when the ice motion varies significantly in the direction normal to the motion, subjecting the ice to rotational forces. These forces may result in phenomena similar to a flaw (q.v.).

110

6. DEFORMATION PROCESSES

6.1   **Fracturing:**   Pressure process whereby ice is permanently deformed, and rupture occurs. Most commonly used to describe breaking across very close ice, compact ice and consolidated ice.

6.2   **Hummocking:**   The pressure process by which sea ice is forced into hummocks. When the floes rotate in the process it is termed screwing.

6.3   **Ridging:**   The pressure process by which sea ice is forced into ridges.

6.4   **Rafting:**   Pressure processes whereby one piece of ice overrides another. Most common in new and young ice (cf. finger rafting).

6.4.1 *FINGER RAFTING:*   Type of rafting whereby interlocking thrusts are formed, each floe thrusting 'fingers' alternately over and under the other. Common in nilas and grey ice.

6.5   **Shore ice ride-up:**   A process by which ice is pushed ashore as a slab.

6.6   **Weathering:**   Processes of ablation and accumulation which gradually eliminate irregularities in an ice surface.

7. OPENINGS IN THE ICE

7.1   **Fracture:**   Any break or rupture through very close ice, compact ice, consolidated ice, fast ice, or a single floe resulting from deformation processes. Fractures may contain brash ice and/or be covered with nilas and/or young ice. Length may vary from a few metres to many kilometres.

7.1.1 *CRACK:*   Any fracture of fast ice, consolidated ice or a single floe which may have been followed by separation ranging from a few centimetres to 1 m.

7.1.1.1 *Tide crack:*   Crack at the line of junction between an immovable ice foot or ice wall and fast ice, the latter subject to rise and fall of the tide.

7.1.1.2 *Flaw:*   A narrow separation zone between drift ice and fast ice, where the pieces of ice are in chaotic state; it forms when drift ice shears under the effect of a strong wind or current along the fast ice boundary (cf. shearing).

7.1.2 *VERY SMALL FRACTURE:*   1–50 m wide.

7.1.3 *SMALL FRACTURE:*   50–200 m wide.

7.1.4 *MEDIUM FRACTURE:*   200–500 m wide.

7.1.5 *LARGE FRACTURE:*   More than 500 m wide.

7.2   **Fracture zone:**   An area which has a great number of fractures.

7.3   **Lead:**   Any fast ice or passageway through sea ice which is navigable by surface vessels.

7.3.1 *SHORE LEAD:*   A lead between drift ice and the shore or between drift ice and an ice front.

7.3.2   *FLAW LEAD:*   A passageway between drift ice and fast ice which is navigable by surface vessels.

7.4   **Polynya:**   Any non-linear shaped opening enclosed in ice. Polynyas may contain brash ice and/or be covered with new ice, nilas or young ice.

7.4.1   *SHORE POLYNYA:*   A polynya between drift ice and the coast or between drift ice and an ice front.

7.4.2   *FLAW POLYNYA:*   A polynya between drift ice and fast ice.

7.4.3   *RECURRING POLYNYA:*   A polynya which recurs in the same position every year.

8. ICE-SURFACE FEATURES

8.1   **Level ice:**   Sea ice which has not been affected by deformation.

8.2   **Deformed ice:**   A general term for ice which has been squeezed together and in places forced upwards (and downwards). Subdivisions are rafted ice, ridged ice and hummocked ice.

8.2.1   *RAFTED ICE:*   Type of deformed ice formed by one piece of ice overriding another (cf. finger rafting).

8.2.1.1   *Finger rafted ice:*   Type of rafted ice in which floes thrust 'fingers' alternately over and under the other.

8.2.2   *RIDGE:*   A line or wall of broken ice forced up by pressure. May be fresh or weathered. The submerged volume of broken ice under a ridge, forced downwards by pressure, is termed an ice keel.

8.2.2.1   *New ridge:*   Ridge newly formed with sharp peaks and slope of sides usually 40°. Fragments are visible from the air at low altitude.

8.2.2.2   *Weathered ridge:*   Ridge with peaks slightly rounded and slope of sides usually 30–40°. Individual fragments are not discernible.

8.2.2.3   *Very weathered ridge:*   Ridge with tops very rounded, slope of sides usually 20–30°.

8.2.2.4   *Aged ridge:*   Ridge which has undergone considerable weathering. These ridges are best described as undulations.

8.2.2.5   *Consolidated ridge:*   A ridge in which the base has frozen together.

8.2.2.6   *Ridged ice:*   Ice piled haphazardly one piece over another in the form of ridges or walls. Usually found in first-year ice (cf. ridging).

8.2.2.6.1   Ridged ice zone: An area in which much ridged ice with similar characteristics has formed.

8.2.2.7   *Shear ridge:*   An ice ridge formation which develops when one ice feature is grinding past another. This type of ridge is more linear than those caused by pressure alone.

8.2.2.7.1   Shear ridge field: Many shear ridges side by side.

8.2.3   *HUMMOCK:*   A hillock of broken ice which has been forced upwards by pressure. May be fresh or weathered. The submerged volume of broken ice under the hummock, forced downwards by pressure, is termed a bummock.

8.2.3.1   *Hummocked ice:*   Sea ice piled haphazardly one piece over another to form an uneven surface. When weathered, has the appearance of smooth hillocks.

8.2.3.2   *Rubble field:*   An area of extremely deformed sea ice of unusual thickness formed during the winter by the motion of drift ice against, or around a protruding rock, islet or other obstruction.

8.3   **Standing floe:**   A separate floe standing vertically or inclined and enclosed by rather smooth ice.

8.4   **Ram:**   An underwater ice projection from an ice wall, ice front, iceberg or floe. Its formation is usually due to a more intensive melting and erosion of the unsubmerged part.

8.5   **Bare ice:**   Ice without snow cover,

8.6   **Snow-covered ice:**   Ice covered with snow.

8.6.1   *SASTRUGI:*   Sharp, irregular ridges formed on a snow surface by wind erosion and deposition. On drift ice the ridges are parallel to the direction of the prevailing wind at the time they were formed.

8.6.2   *SNOWDRIFT:*   An accumulation of wind-blown snow deposited in the lee of obstructions or heaped by wind eddies. A crescent-shaped snowdrift, with ends pointing downwind, is known as a snow barchan.

9. *STAGES OF MELTING*

9.1   **Puddle:**   An accumulation on ice of melt water, mainly due to melting snow, but in the more advanced stages also to the melting of ice. Initial stage consists of patches of melted snow.

9.2   **Thaw hole:**   Vertical holes in sea ice formed when surface puddles melt through to the underlying water.

9.3   **Dried ice:**   Sea ice from the surface of which melt water has disappeared after the formation of cracks and thaw holes. During the period of drying, the surface whitens.

9.4   **Rotten ice:**   Sea ice which has become honeycombed and which is in an advanced state of disintegration.

9.5   **Flooded ice:**   Sea ice which has been flooded by melt water or river water and is heavily loaded by water and wet snow.

9.6   **Shore melt:**   Open water between the shore and the fast ice, formed by melting and/or as a result of river discharge.

10. ICE OF LAND ORIGIN

10.1   **Firn:**   Old snow which has recrystallized into a dense material. Unlike ordinary snow, the particles are to some extent joined together; but, unlike ice, the air spaces in it still connect with each other.

10.2   **Glacier ice:**   Ice in, or originating from, a glacier, whether on land or floating on the sea as icebergs, bergy bits or growlers.

10.2.1   *GLACIER:*   A mass of snow and ice continuously moving from higher to lower ground or, if afloat, continuously spreading. The principal forms of glacier are: inland ice sheets, ice shelves, ice streams, ice caps, ice piedmonts, cirque glaciers and various types of mountain (valley) glaciers.

10.2.2   *ICE WALL:*   An ice cliff forming the seaward margin of a glacier which is not afloat. An ice wall is aground, the rock basement being at or below sea level (cf. ice front).

10.2.3   *ICE STREAM:*   Part of an inland ice sheet in which the ice flows more rapidly and not necessarily in the same direction as the surrounding ice. The margins are sometimes clearly marked by a change in direction of the surface slope but may be indistinct.

10.2.4   *GLACIER TONGUE:*   Projecting seaward extension of a glacier, usually afloat. In the Antarctic, glacier tongues may extend over many tens of kilometres.

10.3   **Ice shelf:**   A floating ice sheet of considerable thickness showing 2–50 m or more above sea level, attached to the coast. Usually of great horizontal extent and with a level or gently undulating surface. Nourished by annual snow accumulation and often also by the seaward extension of land glaciers. Limited areas may be aground. The seaward edge is termed an ice front (q.v.).

10.3.1   *ICE FRONT:*   The vertical cliff forming the seaward face of an ice shelf or other floating glacier varying in height from 2–50 m or more above sea level (cf. ice wall).

10.4   **Calved ice of land origin**

10.4.1   *CALVING:*   The breaking away of a mass of ice from an ice wall, ice front or iceberg.

10.4.2   *ICEBERG:*   A massive piece of ice of greatly varying shape, protruding more than 5 m above sea level, which has broken away from a glacier, and which may be afloat or aground. Icebergs may be described as tabular, dome-shaped, sloping, pinnacled, weathered or glacier bergs.

10.4.2.1 *Glacier berg:*   An irregularly shaped iceberg.

10.4.2.2 *Tabular berg:*   A flat-topped iceberg. Most tabular bergs form by calving from an ice shelf and show horizontal banding (cf. ice island).

10.4.2.3 *Iceberg tongue:*   A major accumulation of icebergs projecting from the coast, held in place by grounding and joined by fast ice.

10.4.3   *ICE ISLAND:*   A large piece of floating ice protruding about 5 m above sea level, which has broken away from an Arctic shelf, having a thickness of 30–50 m and area of from a few thousand square metres to 500 km² or more, and usually characterized by a regularly undulating surface which gives it a ribbed appearance from the air.

10.4.4   *BERGY BIT:*   A large piece of floating glacier ice, generally showing less than 5 m above sea level but more than 1 m and normally about 100–300 m² in area.

10.4.5   *GROWLER:*   Smaller piece of ice than a bergy bit or floeberg, often transparent but appearing green or almost black in colour, extending less than 1 m above the sea surface and normally occupying an area of about 20 m².

11. *SKY AND AIR INDICATIONS*

11.1   **Water sky:**   Dark streaks on the underside of low clouds, indicating the presence of water features in the vicinity of sea ice.

11.2   **Ice blink:**   A whitish glare on low clouds above an accumulation of distant ice.

11.3   **Frost smoke:**   Fog-like clouds due to contact of cold air with relatively warm water, which can appear over openings in the ice, or leeward of the ice edge, and which may persist while ice is forming.

12. *TERMS RELATING TO SURFACE SHIPPING*

12.1   **Beset:**   Situation of a vessel surrounded by ice and unable to move.

12.2   **Ice-bound:**   A harbour, inlet, etc. is said to be ice-bound when navigation by ships is prevented on account of ice, except possibly with the assistance of an icebreaker.

12.3   **Nip:**   Ice is said to nip when it forcibly presses against a ship. A vessel so caught, though undamaged, is said to have been nipped.

12.4   **Ice under pressure:**   Ice in which deformation processes are actively occurring and hence a potential impediment or danger to shipping.

12.5   **Difficult area:**   A general qualitative expression to indicate, in a relative manner, that the severity of ice conditions prevailing in an area is such that navigation in it is difficult.

12.6   **Easy area:**   A general qualitative expression to indicate in a relative manner, that ice conditions prevailing in an area are such that navigation in it is not difficult.

12.7   **Area of weakness:**   A satellite-observed area in which either the ice concentration or the ice thickness is significantly less than that in the surrounding areas. Because the condition is satellite observed, a precise quantitative analysis is not always possible, but navigation conditions are significantly easier than in surrounding areas.

12.8   **Ice port:**   An embayment in an ice front, often of a temporary nature, where ships can moor alongside and unload directly on to the ice shelf.

13.   *TERMS RELATING TO SUBMARINE NAVIGATION*

13.1   **Ice canopy:**   Drift ice from the point of view of the submariner.

13.2   **Friendly ice:**   From the point of view of the submariner, an ice canopy containing many large skylights or other features which permit a submarine to surface. There must be more than ten such features per 30 nautical miles (56 km) along the submarine's track.

13.3   **Hostile ice:**   From the point of view of the submariner, an ice canopy containing no large skylights or other features which permit a submarine to surface.

13.4   **Bummock:**   From the point of view of the submariner, a downward projection from the underside of the ice canopy; the counterpart of a hummock.

13.5   **Ice keel:**   From the point of view of the submariner, a downward-projecting ridge on the underside of the ice canopy; the counterpart of a ridge. Ice keels may extend as much as 50 m below sea-level.

13.6   **Skylight:**   From the point of view of the submariner, thin places in the ice canopy, usually less than 1 m thick and appearing from below as relatively light, translucent patches in dark surroundings. The undersurface of a skylight is normally flat. Skylights are called large if big enough for a submarine to attempt to surface through them (120 m), or small if not.

ICE TERMS ARRANGED IN ALPHABETICAL ORDER

Aged ridge: Ridge which has undergone considerable weathering. These ridges are best described as undulations.

Anchor ice: Submerged ice attached or anchored to the bottom, irrespective of the nature of its formation.

Area of weakness: A satellite-observed area in which either the ice concentration or the ice thickness is significantly less than that in the surrounding areas. Because the condition is satellite observed, a precise quantitative analysis is not always possible, but navigation conditions are significantly easier than in surrounding areas.

Bare ice: Ice without snow cover.

Belt: A large feature of drift ice arrangement; longer than it is wide; from 1 km to more than 100 km in width.

Bergy bit: A large piece of floating glacier ice, generally showing less than 5 m above sea-level but more than 1 m and normally about 100–300 m² in area.

Bergy bit

Bergy water: An area of freely navigable water in which ice of land origin is present in concentrations less than ¹/₁₀. There may be sea ice present, although the total concentration of all ice shall not exceed ¹/₁₀.

Beset: Situation of a vessel surrounded by ice and unable to move.

Big floe: (see Floe).

Bight: An extensive crescent-shaped indentation in the ice edge, formed by either wind or current.

Brash ice: Accumulations of floating ice made up of fragments not more than 2 m across, the wreckage of other forms of ice.

Bummock: From the point of view of the submariner, a downward projection from the underside of the ice canopy; the counterpart of a hummock.

Calving: The breaking away of a mass of ice from an ice wall, ice front or iceberg.

Brash ice

Close ice

Close ice: Floating ice in which the concentration is ⁷⁄₁₀ to ⁸⁄₁₀, composed of floes mostly in contact.

Compacted ice edge: Close, clear-cut ice edge compacted by wind or current; usually on the windward side of an area of drift ice.

Compacting: Pieces of floating ice are said to be compacting when they are subjected to a converging motion, which increases ice concentration and/or produces stresses which may result in ice deformation.

Compact ice: Floating ice in which the concentration is $^{10}/_{10}$ and no water is visible.

Concentration: The ratio expressed in tenths describing the amount of the sea surface covered by ice as a fraction of the whole area being considered. Total concentration includes all stages of development that are present, partial concentration may refer to the amount of a particular stage or of a particular form of ice and represents only a part of the total.

Concentration boundary: A line approximating the transition between two areas of drift ice with distinctly different concentrations.

Consolidated ice: Floating ice in which the concentration is $^{10}/_{10}$ and the floes are frozen together.

Consolidated ice

Consolidated ridge: A ridge in which the base has frozen together.

Crack: Any fracture of fast ice, consolidated ice or a single floe which may have been followed by separation ranging from a few centimetres to 1 m.

Dark nilas: Nilas which is under 5 cm in thickness and is very dark in colour.

Deformed ice: A general term for ice which has been squeezed together and in places forced upwards (and downwards). Subdivisions are rafted ice, ridged ice and hummocked ice.

Difficult area: A general qualitative expression to indicate, in a relative manner, that the severity of ice conditions prevailing in an area is such that navigation in it is difficult.

Diffuse ice edge: Poorly defined ice edge limiting an area of dispersed ice; diverging usually on the leeward side of an area of drift ice.

Diverging: Ice fields or floes in an area are subjected to diverging or dispersive motion, thus reducing ice concentration and/or relieving stresses in the ice.

Dried ice: Sea ice from the surface of which melt water has disappeared after the formation of cracks and thaw holes. During the period of drying, the surface whitens.

Drift ice: Term used in a wide sense to include any area of sea ice, other than fast ice, no matter what form it takes or how it is disposed. When concentrations are high, i.e. 7/10 or more, drift ice may be replaced by the term pack ice.

Easy area: A general qualitative expression to indicate, in a relative manner, that ice conditions prevailing in an area are such that navigation in it is not difficult.

Fast ice: Sea ice which forms and remains fast along the coast, where it is attached to the shore, to an ice wall, to an ice front, between shoals or grounded

British Antarctic Survey

Fast ice

120

icebergs. Vertical fluctuations may be observed during changes of sea level. Fast ice may be formed in situ from sea water or by freezing of floating ice of any age to the shore, and it may extend a few metres or several hundred kilometres from the coast. Fast ice may be more than one year old and may then be prefixed with the appropriate age category (old, second-year, or multi-year). If it is thicker than about 2 m above sea level it is called an ice shelf.

Fast-ice boundary: The ice boundary at any given time between fast ice and drift ice.

Fast-ice edge: The demarcation at any given time between fast ice and open water.

Finger rafted ice: Type of rafted ice in which floes thrust 'fingers' alternately over and under the other.

Finger rafting: Type of rafting whereby interlocking thrusts are formed, each floe thrusting 'fingers' alternately over and under the other. Common in nilas and grey ice.

Firn: Old snow which has recrystallized into a dense material. Unlike ordinary snow, the particles are to some extent joined together; but, unlike ice, the air spaces in it still connect with each other.

First-year ice: Sea ice of not more than one winter's growth, developing from young ice; thickness 30 cm–2 m. May be subdivided into thin first-year ice/white ice, medium first-year ice and thick first-year ice.

Flaw: A narrow separation zone between drift ice and fast ice, where the pieces of ice are in chaotic state; it forms when drift ice shears under the effect of a strong wind or current along the fast ice boundary (cf. shearing).

Flaw lead: A passageway between drift ice and fast ice which is navigable by surface vessels.

Flaw polynya: A polynya between drift ice and fast ice.

Floating ice: Any form of ice found floating in water. The principal kinds of floating ice are lake ice, river ice and sea ice, which form by the freezing of water at the surface, and glacier ice (ice of land origin) formed on land or in an ice shelf. The concept includes ice that is stranded or grounded.

Floe: Any relatively flat piece of sea ice 20 m or more across. Floes are subdivided according to horizontal extent as follows:

GIANT: Over 10 km across.
VAST: 2–10 km across.
BIG: 500–2000 m across.
MEDIUM: 100–500 m across.
SMALL: 20–100 m across.

Floeberg: A massive piece of sea ice composed of a hummock or a group of hummocks, frozen together and separated from any ice surroundings. It may typically protrude up to 5 m above sea level.

Floebit: A relatively small piece of sea ice, normally not more than 10 m across composed of hummocks or parts of ridges frozen together and separated from any surroundings. It typically protrudes up to 2 m above sea level.

Flooded ice: Sea ice which has been flooded by melt water or river water and is heavily loaded by water and wet snow.

Fracture: Any break or rupture through very close ice, compact ice, consolidated ice, fast ice, or a single floe resulting from deformation processes. Fractures may contain brash ice and/or be covered with nilas and/or young ice. Length may vary from a few metres to many kilometres.

> CRACK: 0–1 m wide.
> VERY SMALL FRACTURE: 1–50 m wide.
> SMALL FRACTURE: 50–200 m wide.
> MEDIUM FRACTURE: 200–500 m wide.
> LARGE FRACTURE: more than 500 m wide.

Fracture zone: An area which has a great number of fractures.

Fracturing: Pressure process whereby ice is permanently deformed, and rupture occurs. Most commonly used to describe breaking across very close ice, compact ice and consolidated ice.

Frazil ice: Fine spicules or plates of ice, suspended in water.

Friendly ice: From the point of view of the submariner, an ice canopy containing many large skylights or other features which permit a submarine to surface. There must be more than ten such features per 30 nautical miles (56 km) along the submarine's track.

Frost smoke: Fog-like clouds due to contact of cold air with relatively warm water, which can appear over openings in the ice, or leeward of the ice edge, and which may persist while ice is forming.

Giant floe: (see Floe).

Glacier: A mass of snow and ice continuously moving from higher to lower ground or, if afloat, continuously spreading. The principal forms of glacier are: inland ice sheets, ice shelves, ice streams, ice caps, ice piedmonts, cirque glaciers and various types of mountain (valley) glaciers.

Glacier berg: An irregularly shaped iceberg.

Frost smoke

Glacier ice: Ice in, or originating from, a glacier, whether on land or floating on the sea as icebergs, bergy bits or growlers.

Glacier tongue: Projecting seaward extension of a glacier, usually afloat. In the Antarctic, glacier tongues may extend over many tens of kilometres.

Grease ice: A later stage of freezing than frazil ice when the crystals have coagulated to form a soupy layer on the surface. Grease ice reflects little light, giving the sea a matt appearance.

Grey ice: Young ice 10–15 cm thick. Less elastic than nilas and breaks on swell. Usually rafts under pressure.

Grey-white ice: Young ice 15–30 cm thick. Under pressure more likely to ridge than to raft.

Grounded hummock: Hummocked grounded ice formation. There are single grounded hummocks and lines (or chains) of grounded hummocks.

Growler: Smaller piece of ice than a bergy bit or floeberg, often transparent but appearing green or almost black in colour, extending less than 1 m above the sea surface and normally occupying an area of about 20 m².

Hostile ice: From the point of view of the submariner, an ice canopy containing no large skylights or other features which permit a submarine to surface.

H.M.S. Endurance

Grease Ice

British Antarctic Survey

Grease Ice

Hummock: A hillock of broken ice which has been forced upwards by pressure. May be fresh or weathered. The submerged volume of broken ice under the hummock, forced downwards by pressure, is termed a bummock.

Hummocked ice: Sea ice piled haphazardly one piece over another to form an uneven surface. When weathered, has the appearance of smooth hillocks.

Growler

Hummocking: The pressure process by which sea ice is forced into hummocks. When the floes rotate in the process it is termed screwing.

Iceberg: A massive piece of ice of greatly varying shape, protruding more than 5 m above sea level, which has broken away from a glacier, and which may be afloat or aground. Icebergs may be described as tabular, dome-shaped, sloping, pinnacled, weathered or glacier bergs.

Iceberg tongue: A major accumulation of icebergs projecting from the coast, held in place by grounding and joined together by fast ice.

Ice blink: A whitish glare on low clouds above an accumulation of distant ice.

Ice-bound: A harbour, inlet, etc., is said to be ice-bound when navigation by ships is prevented on account of ice, except possibly with the assistance of an ice-breaker.

Ice boundary: The demarcation at any given time between fast ice and drift ice or between areas of drift ice of different concentrations.

Ice breccia: Ice of different stages of development frozen together.

Ice cake: Any relatively flat piece of sea ice less than 20 m across.

Ice canopy: Drift ice from the point of view of the submariner.

British Antarctic Survey

Tabular iceberg

R.J. Campbell

Weathered iceberg

Ice cover: The ratio of an area of ice of any concentration to the total area of sea surface within some large geographic locale; this locale may be global, hemispheric, or prescribed by a specific oceanographic entity such as Baffin Bay or the Barents Sea.

Ice edge: The demarcation at any given time between the open sea and sea ice of any kind, whether fast or drifting. It may be termed compacted or diffuse (cf. ice boundary).

British Antarctic Survey

Ice blink

British Antarctic Survey

Ice cake and small floes

Ice field: Area of floating ice consisting of any size of floes, which is greater than 10 cm across (cf. patch).

Icefoot: A narrow fringe of ice attached to the coast, unmoved by tides and remaining after the fast ice has moved away.

Ice edge

Ice front

Ice-free: No ice present. If ice of any kind is present this term should not be used.

Ice front: The vertical cliff forming the seaward face of an ice shelf or other floating glacier varying in height from 2–50 m or more above sea level (cf. ice wall).

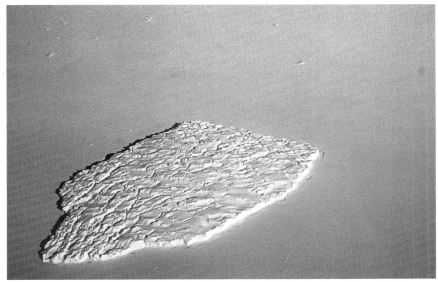

British Antarctic Survey

Ice island

Ice island: A large piece of floating ice protruding about 5 m above sea level, which has broken away from an Arctic ice shelf, having a thickness of 30–50 m and an area of from a few thousand square metres to 500 km^2 or more, and usually characterized by a regularly undulating surface which gives it a ribbed appearance from the air.

Ice isthmus: A narrow connection between two ice areas of very close or compact ice. It may be difficult to pass, whilst sometimes being part of a recommended route.

Ice jam: An accumulation of broken river ice or sea ice caught in a narrow channel.

Ice keel: From the point of view of the submariner, a downward-projecting ridge on the underside of the ice canopy; the counterpart of a ridge. Ice keels may extend as much as 50 m below sea level.

Ice limit: Climatological term referring to the extreme minimum or extreme maximum extent of the ice edge in any given month or period based on observations over a number of years. Term should be preceded by minimum or maximum (cf. mean ice edge).

Ice massif: A variable accumulation of close or very close ice covering hundreds of square kilometres which is found in the same region every summer.

Ice of land origin: Ice formed on land or in an ice shelf, found floating in water. The concept includes ice that is stranded or grounded.

Ice patch: An area of floating ice less than 10 km across.

Ice port: An embayment in an ice front, often of a temporary nature, where ships can moor alongside and unload directly onto the ice shelf.

Ice rind: A brittle shiny crust of ice formed on a quiet surface by direct freezing or from grease ice, usually in water of low salinity. Thickness to about 5 cm. Easily broken by wind or swell, commonly breaking in rectangular pieces.

Ice shelf: A floating ice sheet of considerable thickness showing 2–50 m or more above sea level, attached to the coast. Usually of great horizontal extent and with a level of gently undulating surface. Nourished by annual snow accumulation and often also by the seaward extension of land glaciers. Limited areas may be aground. The seaward edge is termed an ice front (qv).

Ice stream: Part of an inland ice sheet in which the ice flows more rapidly and not necessarily in the same direction as the surrounding ice. The margins are sometimes clearly marked by a change in direction of the surface slope but may be indistinct.

Ice under pressure: Ice in which deformation processes are actively occurring and hence a potential impediment or danger to shipping.

Iceport

Rind ice with hoar-frost on top

Ice wall

Ice wall: An ice cliff forming the seaward margin of a glacier which is not afloat. An ice wall is aground, the rock basement being at or below sea-level (cf. ice front).

Jammed brash barrier: A strip or narrow belt of new, young or brash ice (usually 100–5000 m wide) formed at the edge of either drift or fast ice or at the shore. It is heavily compacted mostly due to wind action and may extend 2–20 m below the surface but does not normally have appreciable topography. Jammed brash barrier may disperse with changing winds but can also consolidate to form a strip of unusually thick ice in comparison with the surrounding drift ice.

Lake ice: Ice formed on a lake, regardless of observed location.

Large fracture: More than 500 m wide.

Large ice field: An ice field over 20 km across.

Lead: Any fracture or passageway through sea ice which is navigable by surface vessels.

Level ice: Sea ice which has not been affected by deformation.

Light nilas: Nilas which is more than 5 cm in thickness and rather lighter in colour than dark nilas.

Mean ice edge: Average position of the ice edge in any given month or period based on observations over a number of years. Other terms which may be used are mean maximum ice edge and mean minimum ice edge (cf. ice limit).

Medium first-year ice: First-year ice 70–120 cm thick.

Medium floe: (see Floe).

British Antarctic Survey

Lead

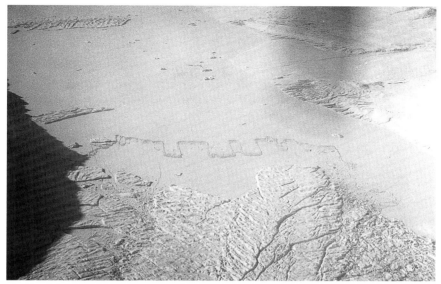

Light nilas and young ice showing finger rafting

Medium fracture: 200–500 m wide.

Medium ice field: An ice field 15–20 km across.

Multi-year ice: Old ice up to 3 m or more thick which has survived at least two summers' melt. Hummocks even smoother than in second-year ice, and the ice is almost salt-free. Colour, where bare, is usually blue. Melt pattern consists of large interconnecting irregular puddles and a well-developed drainage system.

New ice: A general term for recently formed ice which includes frazil ice, grease ice, slush and shuga. These types of ice are composed of ice crystals which are only weakly frozen together (if at all) and have a definite form only while they are afloat.

New ridge: Ridge newly formed with sharp peaks and slope of sides usually 40°. Fragments are visible from the air at low altitude.

Nilas: A thin elastic crust of ice, easily bending on waves and swell and under pressure, thrusting in a pattern of interlocking 'fingers' (finger rafting). Has a matt surface and is up to 10 cm in thickness. May be subdivided into dark nilas and light nilas.

Nip: Ice is said to nip when it forcibly presses against a ship. A vessel so caught, though undamaged, is said to have been nipped.

Old ice: Sea ice which has survived at least one summer's melt; typical thickness up to 3 m or more. Most topographic features are smoother than on first-year ice. May be subdivided into second-year ice and multi-year ice.

Old ice

Open ice

Open ice: Floating ice in which the ice concentration is $^4/_{10}$ to $^6/_{10}$, with many leads and polynyas, and the floes are generally not in contact with one another.

Open water: A large area of freely navigable water in which sea ice is present in concentrations less than $^1/_{10}$. No ice of land origin is present.

134

Pancake ice

Pancake ice: Predominantly circular pieces of ice from 30 cm–3 m in diameter, and up to about 10 cm in thickness, with raised rims due to the pieces striking against one another. It may be formed on a slight swell from grease ice, shuga or slush or as a result of the breaking of ice rind, nilas or, under severe conditions of swell or waves, of grey ice. It also sometimes forms at some depth, at an interface between water bodies of different physical characteristics, from where it floats to the surface; its appearance may rapidly cover wide areas of water.

Polynya: Any non-linear shaped opening enclosed in ice. Polynyas may contain brash ice and/or be covered with new ice, nilas or young ice.

Puddle: An accumulation on ice of melt water, mainly due to melting snow, but in the more advanced stages also to the melting of ice. Initial stage consists of patches of melted snow.

Rafted ice: Type of deformed ice formed by one piece of ice overriding another (cf. finger rafting).

Rafting: Pressure processes whereby one piece of ice overrides another. Most common in new and young ice (cf. finger rafting).

Ram: An underwater ice projection from an ice wall, ice front, iceberg or floe. Its formation is usually due to a more intensive melting and erosion of the unsubmerged part.

Recurring polynya: A polynya which recurs in the same position every year.

135

Ram

Ridge: A line or wall of broken ice forced up by pressure. May be fresh or weathered. The submerged volume of broken ice under a ridge, forced downwards by pressure, is termed an ice keel.

Ridge ice: Ice piled haphazardly one piece over another in the form of ridges or walls. Usually found in first-year ice (cf. ridging).

Ridged ice zone: An area in which ridged ice with similar characteristics has formed.

Ridging: The pressure process by which sea ice is forced into ridges.

River ice: Ice formed on a river, regardless of observed location.

Rotten ice: Sea ice which has become honeycombed and which is in an advanced state of disintegration.

Rubble field: An area of extremely deformed sea ice of unusual thickness formed during the winter by the motion of drift ice against, or around a protruding rock, islet or other obstruction.

Sastrugi: Sharp, irregular ridges formed on a snow surface by wind erosion and deposition. On drift ice the ridges are parallel to the direction of the prevailing wind at the time they were formed.

Sea ice: Any form of ice found at sea which has originated from the freezing of sea water.

136

Sastrugi

Second-year ice: Old ice which has survived only one summer's melt; typical thickness up to 2.5 m and sometimes more. Because it is thicker than first-year ice, it stands higher out of the water. In contrast to multi-year ice, summer melting produces a regular pattern of numerous small puddles. Bare patches and puddles are usually greenish-blue.

Shearing: An area of drift ice is subject to shear when the ice motion varies significantly in the direction normal to the motion, subjecting the ice to rotational forces. These forces may result in phenomena similar to a flaw (qv).

Shear ridge: An ice ridge formation which develops when one ice feature is grinding past another. This type of ridge is more linear than those caused by pressure alone.

Shear ridge field: Many shear ridges side by side.

Shore ice ride-up: A process by which ice is pushed ashore as a slab.

Shore lead: A lead between drift ice and the shore or between drift ice and an ice front.

Shore melt: Open water between the shore and the fast ice, formed by melting and/or as a result of river discharge.

Shore polynya: A polynya between drift ice and the coast or between drift ice and an ice front.

British Antarctic Survey

Shuga

Shuga: An accumulation of spongy white ice lumps, a few centimetres across; they are formed from grease ice or slush and sometimes from anchor ice rising to the surface.

Skylight: From the point of view of the submariner, thin places in the ice canopy, usually less than 1 m thick and appearing from below as relatively light, translucent patches in dark surroundings. The undersurface of a skylight is normally flat. Skylights are called large if big enough for a submarine to attempt to surface through them (120 m), or small if not.

Slush: Snow which is saturated and mixed with water on land or ice surfaces, or as a viscous floating mass in water after a heavy snowfall.

Small floe: (see Floe).

Small fracture: 50–200 m wide.

Small ice cake: An ice cake less than 2 m across.

Small ice field: An ice field 10–15 km across.

Snow-covered ice: Ice covered with snow.

Snowdrift: An accumulation of wind-blown snow deposited in the lee of obstructions or heaped by wind eddies. A crescent-shaped snowdrift, with ends pointing down-wind, is known as a snow barchan.

138

Standing floe: A separate floe standing vertically or inclined and enclosed by rather smooth ice.

Stranded ice: Ice which has been floating and has been deposited on the shore by retreating high water.

Strip: Long narrow area of floating ice, about 1 km or less in width, usually composed of small fragments detached from the main mass of ice, and run together under the influence of wind, swell or current.

Tabular berg: A flat-topped iceberg. Most tabular bergs form by calving from an ice shelf and show horizontal banding (cf. ice island).

Thaw holes: Vertical holes in sea ice formed when surface puddles melt through to the underlying water.

Thick first-year ice: First-year ice over 120 cm thick.

Thin first-year ice/white ice: First-year ice 30–70 cm thick.

Thin first-year ice/white ice first stage: 30–50 cm thick.

Thin first-year ice/white ice second stage: 50–70 cm thick.

Tide crack: Crack at the line of junction between an immovable ice foot or ice wall and fast ice, the latter subject to rise and fall of the tide.

Tongue: A projection of the ice edge up to several kilometres in length, caused by wind or current.

Vast floe: (see Floe).

Very close ice: Floating ice in which the concentration is $9/10$ to less than $10/10$.

Very open ice: Floating ice in which the concentration is $1/10$ to $3/10$ and water preponderates over ice.

Very small fracture: 1–50 m wide.

Very weathered ridge: Ridge with tops very rounded, slope of sides usually 20–30°.

Water sky: Dark streaks on the underside of low clouds, indicating the presence of water features in the vicinity of sea ice.

Weathered ridge: Ridge with peaks slightly rounded and slope of sides usually 30–40°. Individual fragments are not discernible.

British Antarctic Survey

Very close ice

British Antarctic Survey

Very open ice

Weathering: Processes of ablation and accumulation which gradually eliminate irregularities in an ice surface.

White ice: See Thin first-year ice.

Young coastal ice: The initial stage of fast ice formation consisting of nilas or young ice, its width varying from a few metres up to 100–200 m from the shoreline.

Young ice: Ice in the transition stage between nilas and first-year ice, 10–30 cm in thickness. May be subdivided into grey ice and grey-white ice.

140

CHAPTER 8

THE OBSERVATION OF PHENOMENA

Introduction

The seaman has unusual opportunities for observing natural phenomena of all kinds. This can be made an interesting hobby, and the observer may be lucky enough, sooner or later, to make a rare, or even unique, observation, which if carefully observed and recorded, will contribute to scientific knowledge. The comparative frequency or rarity of certain phenomena is indicated in this and the four following chapters, as far as our present knowledge goes. Phenomena of unknown origin are occasionally seen at sea and these should be carefully observed and recorded.

It is however not only the rare observations which are of value. All meteorological phenomena, whether optical or general, are directly related to the state of the atmosphere and weather prevailing at the time, and their recording in the Additional Remarks section of the *Ship's Meteorological Logbook* helps to complete the information given by routine observations. Also, there is probably still a good deal to be learnt about many of the more common phenomena, including their frequency and geographical distribution, for which purpose it is obvious that all observations made in any part of the world should be put on record.

Hints are given in these chapters on the observations or measurements which are necessary if the phenomenon is to be correctly identified. Observations are much more valuable if accompanied by drawings or sketches, in black and white or colour, or by photographs. If there is not room in the log, the observations and sketches can be attached to it.

The more interesting and unusual observations and illustrations are published in *The Marine Observer*. Notes and sketches on phenomena which are outside the scope of the Met. Office are always sent on to the relevant authority for examination and comment.

Methods of observation. Some optical phenomena such as coronae and iridescent cloud appear to be very near the sun or moon. Those near the sun may not be seen at all unless the eyes are shaded from direct sunlight. Apart from this, optical phenomena such as haloes, coronae, etc., viewed in the daytime, when the sky is often very bright, are more easily seen if the amount of light entering the eye is reduced, and sometimes a very faint halo etc., can only be seen if this is done. The sky may be viewed through neutral-tinted glass of a light tone, such as the lightest of those on a sextant, or the reflection from black glass may be used, if available, or from a piece of ordinary glass painted on one side with black enamel or backed with black paper. If a pair of ordinary sun-glasses of suitable colour is available, this is the best method of all. Yellow-brown, not too deep, has been found to be very satisfactory. Glasses of this colour have the power of slightly increasing contrast, so as to show distant land more distinctly on a misty day. The natural colour of any phenomenon is, of course, modified by these. The same methods also give a better view of clouds, of the details in a bright cloud mass, or of the very faint extensions, near the limit of visibility, of cloud in a blue sky.

There is a useful tip for seeing any very faint light at night, which is near or just beyond the limit of direct visibility. Do not look directly at the object, or where you suspect it to be, but fix the attention on a point a little way above, below, or to the side of it. Then view the spot 'out of the corner of the eye'. Light will thus be seen that would otherwise be invisible or, if it is directly visible, it will appear brighter by this process of 'averted' or 'oblique' vision. This applies to very faint light of every sort, whether concentrated in a point or diffused, such as faint terrestrial lights, faint stars, comets' tails, all zodiacal light phenomena and the fainter parts of aurorae.

In the case of phenomena of considerable duration, it is best to make notes of the various appearances as they are seen to come into view, or of other changes, carefully recording the times throughout the progress of the phenomenon. This is preferable to trusting to the memory afterwards. Rough sketches can also be made at the time and subsequently worked up into finished drawings or sketches. If colour is to be used, notes of the various colours should be made at the time.

It is desirable that observations be accompanied by sketches and/or photographs in colour or black and white, whenever possible. These will often show detail that cannot be put into words. Sketches may be made either in ink or in pencil; in some cases delicacy of shading or fine detail is better rendered in pencil. When chosen for reproduction in *The Marine Observer*, the sketches will be redrawn. Although as full a report as possible is desirable, photographs taken by any members of the ship's company or passengers are acceptable, especially for publication. All that is asked for the record is the date, UTC, latitude and longitude or geographical position, identification of the object and names of the observers and photographers. Copyright of published material, including photographs, remains with the originator.

An accurate account of the size and relative positions of the main features of what is seen is the prime requirement. Angular measurements are necessary in many cases for the identification of the phenomenon, as explained in the subsequent chapters. These are best incorporated in the written observation, unless the accompanying sketch is purely a diagrammatic one.

Phenomena such as haloes, rainbows and waterspouts may be photographed, giving a sufficiently short exposure, such as would best show cloud detail. The best results, particularly in the case of coloured objects, can only be obtained by the use of colour film or panchromatic film of suitable speed with a suitable colour filter over the lens. The same remarks apply to mirage, which has very rarely been photographed, though there appears to be no reason why satisfactory results should not be obtained.

OBSERVATIONS BY RADAR

With radar sets working on 3 cm or 10 cm having a suitable form of presentation, echoes are obtained from rain up to distances of 40 n. mile or more. In this way showers, fronts and thunderstorms may be located and warning given of their approach. Echoes from cloud have been reported, but these are probably due to rain or drizzle within the cloud and not to the cloud particles themselves.

Objects at ground level or sea level are normally visible on the radar screen at distances a little beyond the visible horizon, owing to refraction. In certain conditions, however, much greater ranges are obtained. This occurs most frequently over the sea, and is due to a temperature inversion near the surface and/or a fall of humidity with height which causes reflection or abnormal refraction of the rays.

The reverse effect, i.e. a smaller degree of refraction (or sub-refraction) than is usual can occur owing to a very pronounced temperature lapse-rate and/or an increase of humidity with height. Sub-refraction however is neither a very marked nor frequent phenomenon.

Ordinary meteorological fronts are not a major cause of abnormal radar ranges. Due to absorption of the radio energy, very heavy rain may tend to mask a radar target behind the rain area; this effect is unlikely to be significant on a wavelength of 10 cm but it may become important at shorter wavelengths.

The use of radar as a means of detection of ice should be borne in mind. In normal meteorological conditions, echoes from most bergs may be detected at a useful range, but in certain meteorological conditions sub-refraction may occur and normal detection ranges be appreciably reduced. It has also been found that at times, even under favourable conditions, a very poor echo has been obtained from quite a large berg, the inclination of the slope presented to the observer apparently having an effect upon its reflecting properties, which is of as much account as the length or height of the berg. Bergy bits, growlers or pieces of pack ice, especially if smoothed by weathering, may pass undetected in strong sea clutter, even if they are large enough to sink or damage ships. On the other hand, in conditions where sea clutter is well marked, the cessation of such echoes may indicate the presence of pack ice.

Radar can therefore only be considered as an additional aid to the navigator in the detection of ice but it must be clearly understood that an absence of indication on the screen does not necessarily mean the absence of dangerous ice in the neighbourhood of the vessel.

CHAPTER 9

ASTRONOMICAL PHENOMENA

ECLIPSES

Partial eclipses of the sun or moon provide interesting spectacles but afford no opportunity for the seaman to make observations of particular value. Little diminution in sunlight is perceived until more than half the sun's disc is covered by the moon. An appreciable fall of temperature occurs during a large partial eclipse of the sun.

Solar Eclipse. A total eclipse of the sun is perhaps the grandest of all natural phenomena. While almost of annual occurrence, its visibility on any occasion is confined to a very small area, along a line usually less than 100 n. mile wide, so that in any fixed place it is in general very rare. The duration of the total phase is very short, usually from a few seconds up to about two minutes, though in very exceptional circumstances it may be considerably more, the possible maxima being nearly eight minutes. During totality the fall of temperature is marked; often the wind changes or springs up, if previously calm. The sky darkens and has a peculiar appearance, often with lurid cloud colours. During totality the bright planets and the brighter stars may be seen.

Very occasionally a ship at sea or in harbour may be on the line of totality and several of such observations have been received in the last 50 years. The seaman fortunate enough to witness such an eclipse should endeavour to record all that he sees in as full detail as possible. There is so much to see in such a short time that it is desirable for several persons to observe in company. At the instant the moon finally covers the round body of the sun normally seen, the solar corona will spring into view. This is an irregularly extended atmosphere of the sun, pearly-white in colour, giving about half as much light as the full moon. It has a definite shape which varies according to the position of the year of observation in the 11-year cycle of solar activity (see under Sunspots).

Near the time of maximum activity the corona is disposed fairly equally round the sun, with a definite structure of rays and bands, and sometimes curved forms like flower petals. Near the time of minimum activity the corona shows much less structural detail and the form is quite different. A wide band, more or less parallel sided, stretches outward from the equatorial region of the sun, one on each side of the sun, and these bands may extend a long distance, up to two or more solar diameters. At this time the polar regions usually show only a few short rays of coronal light. In the intermediate years of the solar cycle, the corona assumes forms intermediate between those described above.

Owing to the short duration of total solar eclipses and their comparative rarity, the total time for which the corona has been seen in the last 150 years is probably about two hours. Its exact form on any particular occasion is unpredictable. Marine observers can therefore make observations of real scientific value if the form, extent and detail of the corona is carefully noted and sketched. As the fainter extensions of the corona are best seen with the unaided eye and the structural detail is best seen with binoculars or a small telescope, it is best, especially when the duration of totality is short, to have two observers, each working in one of these different ways.

One or more of the great rose-red eruptions of hydrogen and calcium gas from the sun, known as prominences, may be seen adjacent to the moon's limb without optical assistance, especially if the sun is near its state of maximum activity. Unlike the corona, these may be seen in full sunlight on any day, by astronomers using special apparatus. Other features of a total eclipse on which attention may be concentrated are (a) meteorological effects (b) the changing colour effects of sky and cloud and the rapid onrush of the moon's shadow through the air as the total phase begins, (c) the visibility of planets and stars.

World Solar Eclipses. For information on the schedule of expected solar eclipses, both total and annular up to the year 2015, see Appendix IV.

Lunar Eclipse. The total phase of a lunar eclipse generally lasts a considerable time, sometimes for nearly two hours; the exact duration depends on how centrally the moon passes through the Earth's shadow. The totally eclipsed moon usually remains visible, appearing in some shade of red or copper. Careful observation of this colour, and its changes, if any, during the total phase are of value. A general statement of the degree of brightness of the totally eclipsed moon should also be given, noting how far its surface markings remain visible. The totally eclipsed moon receives reddish sunlight by refraction through the section of the Earth's atmosphere in profile to the moon at the time, and the amount and colour of the refracted light vary according to the cloudiness and other meteorological conditions in this part of the atmosphere. When fine dust in sufficient quantity is suspended in the air after a big volcanic eruption, the moon may almost, or even completely, disappear from sight during total eclipse. Such an observation should be carefully recorded, with all relevant detail.

COMETS

Comets are members of the Solar System, moving in elliptical orbits, in most cases so enormously elongated that the period of revolution round the sun may be hundreds or even thousands of years. A few return in a comparatively short time one of these being the well-known Halley's Comet, with a period of about 76 years, last seen in 1985/6.

Comets are much less dense than planets, and consist of a loose aggregation of widely separated small solid bodies, ranging from the size of a grain of sand to that of small stones, probably with an admixture of larger pieces. The diameter of this collection is usually only a few hundred miles, but may be several thousand. Comets are only seen in that part of their orbit near the sun, when they shine partly by reflected light but mainly by the vaporizing of the material of the comet by the sun's heat. An interesting feature of a comet is its tail, which is only formed when the comet is relatively near the sun. This consists of dust and gases ejected from the head, probably by light pressure and electrical repulsion. The tail of a large comet may be many millions of miles in actual length. The apparent length may be anything from a degree or two to 60° or 80° or more. The direction of the tail is from the comet's head away from the sun. This direction bears no relation to the direction of the movement of the head of the comet in its orbit. The tail of a comet, unlike the transitory trail of a meteor, therefore does not show the direction in which the comet has travelled.

Most comets never become bright enough to be seen without telescopic aid and some never develop tails, but a bright comet is a magnificent naked-eye spectacle. There should be no confusion between the appearance of a comet and a meteor. A meteor is only seen for a few seconds as it travels more or less rapidly over its apparent path in the sky. A comet remains apparently fixed among the stars and sets with them in due course. It has a continuous movement relative to the stars, but in most cases this can only be seen in a naked-eye or binocular observation by comparing its position on successive nights. The period of naked-eye visibility of a comet may be anything from a few days to a number of weeks. It finally becomes invisible by either getting too faint, or passing into the daylight region of the sky or changing in declination so as to sink below the horizon.

Astronomers measure the position of the head of a comet relative to stars near it in the field of view of a telescope, or large-scale photographs may be taken. From a minimum of three such observations on successive nights, the comet's orbit in space and its subsequent apparent track in the sky can be computed. Angular distances of the comet from two or three bright stars, measured by sextant, are not sufficiently accurate for this purpose, but serve to identify the object and help in making an accurate sketch of the comet and its tail in relation to the stars. It may occasionally happen that more than one naked-eye comet is visible at the same time.

Valuable observations of a naked-eye comet may be made at sea, and it may happen that some interesting feature is seen which would not otherwise be put on record, if conditions of daylight or cloud make observations impossible in other parts of the world at that particular time. The brightness of the head and the form and length of the tail may sometimes change appreciably from night to night. The brightness of the head is estimated by comparison with that of neighbouring stars or planets, as described under Novae below. The altitude of the comet's head should be given, as part of this observation, also notes on the state of the sky, such as whether thin cloud, haze, twilight or moonlight is present. Careful sketches of the form and length of the tail are valuable and should include details of the structure of the tail, if any are seen, stating whether the observation was made with the unaided eye, or with binoculars. The end of the tail usually fades very gradually into the dark sky and the method of averted vision (see page 142) can be used to see it as far as possible; binoculars will not show the fainter extension. It is of special importance to record any tails, other than the main one, which may be visible; these are normally on the same side of the head as the main tail, making various angles with it, and they are usually narrower and fainter than the main tail. On rare occasions a short tail pointing towards the sun may be seen, i.e. in a direction opposite to that of the main tail. If the comet shows any peculiarity of colour this should be noted.

THE ZODIACAL LIGHT AND ASSOCIATED PHENOMENA

The zodiacal light
This is observed as the cone-shaped extremity of an elongated ellipse of soft whitish light which extends from the sun as centre, extending above the westerly horizon in

the evening or the easterly horizon in the morning. The best time for observation is just after the last traces of twilight have disappeared in the evening, or just before the first traces appear in the morning. The light retains its apparent place among the stars and gradually sets or rises with them. It is more brilliant in the tropics, but is very conspicuous even in temperate latitudes, if observed away from the glare of large towns.

The axis of the light lies in the zodiac, very nearly but not quite in the plane of the ecliptic. In tropical latitudes, where the ecliptic makes a large angle with the horizon at all times of the year, the light may be seen well on any clear night or morning in all months. In the temperate latitudes of the Northern Hemisphere it is best seen in the evenings of January to March and in the mornings of September to November.

The light is pearly and homogeneous and differs markedly in quality from that of the Milky Way, the brightest part of which it may considerably exceed in luminosity. Its luminosity decreases with altitude above the horizon, since its brightness is greater the nearer the observed point is to the sun's position below the horizon. It appears, however, to fall off in brightness near the horizon on account of the greater thickness of the atmosphere its light has to traverse. At any altitude the axis of the light is brighter than its lateral parts. In northern temperate latitudes the edge of the cone towards the north in azimuth is less well-defined than that towards the south and tends to spread northwards near the horizon.

The zodiacal light is believed to be a cosmic phenomenon, due to the reflection of the sun's light from dust or gaseous matter, extending outwards to a point somewhat beyond the Earth's orbit. There is much that is not known about this phenomenon and new observations from all latitudes will be of real value. Any features of interest should be noted, such as the colour of the light and any irregularity of form or light distribution. Observations of its brightness will be of value, as it is not yet known whether this is constant on successive nights or in different years. Apparent changes of brightness often occur since the night sky is not always equally transparent. The presence of a bright planet, especially Venus, in the region of the light dims it considerably. Estimates of brightness should be made on moonless nights, after all twilight has disappeared, by comparing the light with that of the Milky Way, preferably at about the same altitude. The position of the Milky Way should be specified, as this varies markedly in brightness in different parts of the sky. Thus the light on a given night might be estimated to be twice as bright as the Milky Way in Cygnus.

Observations of the precise position of the light, about which there is still some uncertainty, may be made by a careful sketch of the cone showing the position of specified stars, either within, on the edge of, or outside the cone.

Zodiacal band and Gegenschein. Joining the apexes of the cones of the morning and evening zodiacal lights is an extremely faint luminous band, a few degrees wide, lying along or nearly along the ecliptic, called the zodiacal band. On this band, at a point very nearly or exactly 180° from the sun's position in the ecliptic, is a somewhat brighter and larger but ill-defined patch, 10° or more in diameter, known by the German name 'Gegenschein'. This therefore is due south (in the Northern Hemisphere) at midnight, local time. These phenomena may be observed in temperate latitudes on the clearest moonless nights when at sufficient altitude; they are somewhat brighter in the tropics, on account of the greater altitude of the ecliptic. Further observations of these phenomena are much desired, especially from tropical localities. The track and width of the band, and the size, shape and position of the Gegenschein should be noted, together with variations of brilliancy and any special features seen, but the observation will be found difficult even to keen eyesight. The Gegenschein is usually invisible for the few nights on which it is projected upon the Milky Way in its annual journey round the ecliptic.

NOVAE

Sometimes, quite unpredictably, a small star, usually such that a telescope is required to sight it, brightens up very much, within a few hours or a day or two at the most. This is, somewhat loosely, called a 'nova' or 'new star'. While many of these never become visible to the naked eye, occasionally one does so and may even reach the first magnitude, or brighter, thus completely changing the aspect of the constellation in which it appears. If conspicuous, a nova is generally mentioned in the newspapers. Should the marine observer hear of one, or discover one (in which case he will usually find he is not the first discoverer) he may be interested in following its changes of brightness. The normal history of a nova is that it remains at full brightness for a short time, probably a day or two at the most, and then very gradually decreases, the reduction in brightness being interrupted by slight temporary increases. If the star has attained the third magnitude or more it may remain visible to the naked eye for several weeks.

If the observer wishes to record the exact brightness of a nova (or other star) at any time, he may select a star of about the same altitude judged to be exactly of the same brightness. If no such star is available, he should select two stars of about the same altitude as the nova, one a little brighter and one a little fainter than the nova. He can then express the brightness of the nova in terms of the small interval of brightness between the two comparison stars. For example, it might be halfway between them in brightness, or one-third of the interval, counting from the brighter to the fainter, or one-quarter of the interval, counting from the fainter to the brighter. If such an observation is received, it can be easily converted into actual magnitudes, since the magnitudes of all naked-eye stars have been accurately determined. Both these methods break down if the star is much above the first magnitude, as suitable comparison stars would probably not be available. One or more of the bright planets, if visible, might, however, serve for this purpose.

An accurate observation of the magnitude of a nova, especially in its early stages when the brightness is changing quickly, may be of great value to astronomers, since no other observation might have been made anywhere else at the same time.

SUNSPOTS

It is very dangerous to the sight to look at the sun, either with or without optical aid, without using smoked or deeply tinted glass to reduce the light. This applies even when the sun is in partial eclipse. The only exception is when the sunlight is greatly weakened by passage through fairly thick fog, especially when the sun is at low altitude.

The number and size of sunspots varies in different years. Over a period of years solar activity, of which the occurrence of large sunspots is one manifestation, rises to a maximum and subsequently falls to a minimum. The time between successive maxima varies considerably, but averages about 11 years. For several years around the time of maximum activity, spots are frequently large enough to be seen without optical aid; sometimes two or more are thus visible at the same time. Around the time of minimum activity, spots are either very small or completely absent. The life of an individual spot may be anything from a few days to several weeks.

Owing to the sun's rotation on its axis, a spot previously formed, and coming into view at the sun's eastern limb, will appear to cross the disc in about 14 days, if it lasts so long. Apparent changes of position of the spots on the sun's disc take place during the day, but are merely due to the observer's changing angle of view. The imaginary line forming the horizontal diameter of the sun at noon appears to be tilted upward between sunrise and noon and downward between noon and sunset, the most extreme tilting occurring at sunrise and sunset.

Daily photographs of the sun through telescopes are taken at one or other of the astronomical observatories throughout the world. While marine observers may find it interesting to see the spots and note their changes of form and position on successive days, especially in years of maximum solar activity, it is not necessary to make sketches of them in the logbook as these can never be accurate enough to have any scientific value.

Solar flares. Near certain sunspots there occur areas which undergo sudden increases in brightness; these are called flares. They are best seen by means of special instruments which give a picture of the sun's surface in red hydrogen light. Some of the greatest solar flares have, however, been observed as increases in the total white light of the sun; seen in this way, a flare lasts for a few minutes and has about the same area as a large sunspot. The first such observation of the bright patch on the sun's surface was made in 1859 and several flares have been similarly observed since then. The appearance of flares cannot be predicted, but they are more numerous at times of maximum solar activity (as measured by the numbers of sunspots).

The increase in light intensity during a flare is particularly strong in the ultraviolet part of the spectrum (the part beyond the visible violet light to which our eyes are not sensitive). The blast of ultraviolet light emitted from a solar flare produces several detectable effects in the high atmosphere of the Earth.

Associated with the increase in light intensity during a flare, there is ejection of material particles from the region of the flare out into space. This material shoots out at speeds of about 300 to 650 kilometres per second, which probably increases as the material gets further from the sun. If moving in the appropriate direction, this material causes interesting effects in the high atmosphere. Some of the high atmospheric effects of solar flares are described in the next chapter.

CHAPTER 10

PHENOMENA OF THE HIGH ATMOSPHERE

Regions of the high atmosphere
The high atmosphere of the Earth is classified into regions according to the degree of ionization of the atoms of the atmospheric gases at the level concerned, that is, according to the electrical conductivity. In the lower atmosphere air is a very good electrical insulator, i.e. its conductivity is very low. In the high atmosphere, however, many of the atoms are ionized so that the air is electrically conducting. The classification into regions depends on the different degrees of conductivity and other electrical properties at the different levels. There are three regions of the following approximate heights: the D region, between 48 and 80 km up; the E region, between 80 and 130 km; and the F region above 130 km.

High-frequency radio fadeouts
Long-distance radio transmission in the short-wave band (say in the frequency range from 3 to 30 megahertz) is normally achieved by reflection of the radiation from the F region, the main influence of the D and E regions being to absorb some of the energy of the radio waves. When the blast of ultraviolet light from a solar flare reaches the Earth it increases the ionization in the D region, however, and this increased ionization causes absorption of HF signals, reducing the signal strength considerably or even causing a complete fadeout of the received signals. Such a HF radio fadeout can occur only on the daylight hemisphere of the Earth; it usually lasts for about twenty minutes.

Sudden enhancements of atmospherics
Lightning flashes in the lower atmosphere are a source of radio noise, detected over a wide range of frequencies as the crackles called atmospherics. Thunderstorms and lightning flashes are most numerous in the tropics, and transmission of the resultant radio noise around the Earth to higher latitudes is by means of reflection from the various conducting regions of the high atmosphere. For the low-frequency (LF) part of atmospherics (in the frequency range below 100 kilohertz) it is the D region which acts as the reflector. Following a solar flare and the consequent increased ionization in the D region, the reflection of LF atmospherics is suddenly improved and the noise level of atmospherics may rise to as much as double its normal value. The rise takes place in a few minutes and the level remains high for an hour or two.

High-frequency radio blackouts
When the material ejected from the sun during solar flares, and at other times, reaches the Earth, it affects the electrical properties of the F region in such a way that it ceases to act as a good reflector for HF radio. This effect is called an ionospheric storm. It is most severe in high latitudes because the material particles coming from the sun are electrically charged and are guided to the polar regions by the Earth's magnetic field. Since they are often connected with solar flares, ionospheric storms are more frequent during solar activity maxima, but this is not

always the case. The HF radio blackout associated with a severe ionospheric storm may last for several days.

Magnetic disturbances

The Earth's magnetic field is almost entirely of internal origin, being most probably produced by electric currents flowing in the molten material of the core, but there is a small part of it (less than one hundredth) which can be attributed to electric currents flowing in the high atmosphere. It is believed that these currents flow mainly in the E region. The daily heating of the atmosphere by the sun causes the currents to go through a regular daily cycle of change. These regular changes are very small in most places and cannot be detected by an ordinary compass needle, the maximum change of direction of the needle during a day being about one-fifth of a degree of arc.

Quicker changes occur at the times of HF radio fadeouts, but they also are too small to be detected by a compass needle. They are known as magnetic crochets or as solar flare effects.

Much larger deviations can occur, however. They are the result of large, irregular changes in the E layer currents, called magnetic storms, which occur in conjunction with ionospheric storms and HF radio blackouts in high latitudes. Like the ionospheric storms of the F region these E region magnetic storms are caused by the arrival of the material particles ejected from the sun during solar flares and at other times.

If the magnetic storm is severe, the compass needle may be deflected continuously in one direction, to the extent of about half a degree, for some hours. In more intense storms the needle may oscillate one degree or more on either side of its normal position, and such oscillation may continue for as long as ten or twenty minutes before dying out. Further oscillation may occur after a period of quiescence, and deviations of 2° or more have been known, though these are rare. During the great magnetic storm of 25 January 1938 a deviation of 4° eastward was observed off the Portuguese coast.

AIRGLOW

On a clear starlit night, in the absence of normal or abnormal twilight, moonlight, lunar twilight, thin high cloud over the sky, auroral displays or artificial illumination from towns, etc., the sky background is not dark, but has a certain degree of luminosity. While some of this luminosity is due to the combined light of stars too faint to be seen individually without the aid of a telescope, the greater part is due to a faint glow known as the airglow. Older names for this were 'permanent aurora' and 'earthlight'.

The airglow is generally uniform over the sky except towards the horizon where it is usually somewhat brighter. The intensity is not always the same on different nights and there are exceptional nights when the sky background appears to be unusually light. There are no means of estimating the intensity of the glow by visual observation, so that the phenomenon is not one which can be usefully observed at sea.

ARTIFICIAL SATELLITES AND RESEARCH ROCKETS

Artificial Satellites — Launches and Decays

By the end of 1989 no less than 3196 successful launches had been made, the current annual launch rate being about 120. These figures do not reflect the number of objects which actually achieved orbit. In addition to the actual satellites, there are the discarded rocket cases, fragments from break-ups, and many smaller objects referred to generally as 'space junk'. Although many decay, about 7000 objects are routinely tracked by military radar installations. It is estimated that about 10% of these objects are above the horizon at any one time but only a small percentage of these can be seen with the naked eye or binoculars. Satellites can be seen when the observer's sky is dark but the object is still illuminated by the Sun. Such situations exist normally in the evening shortly after sunset and in the morning just before sunrise. Bright satellites can usually be seen when the Sun is at least 6° below the horizon.

When seen, a satellite appears as a pinpoint of light (stellar appearance) moving slowly across the sky. These objects can readily be distinguished from meteors and fireballs because the latter take just 3 or 4 seconds to cross the sky, whereas bright artificial satellites take much longer, possibly up to 45 minutes. The lowest satellites, at heights of a few hundred kilometres, orbit the Earth in about 90 minutes and from a position on the surface of the Earth, they move at a rate of about 2° per second, that is about 4 moon diameters per second.

The brightness of a satellite depends on many factors and the light may be constant. A tumbling rocket case (shaped approximately like a milk bottle) will present varying aspects to the Sun and the observer, and hence may appear to flash. A large flat surface on a satellite can produce exceedingly bright irregular flashes.

The above notes are given as an aid to identifying a sighting as a man-made object, and there is no need to record these in the meteorological logbook. However, towards the end of a satellite's life it will enter the denser regions of the Earth's atmosphere and decay or burn up like a natural chunk of rock. These decays are of great interest and accurate reports of these events are extremely important and should be logged in the greatest detail possible. A fireball produced by the decay of a satellite and that from a natural object can easily be distinguished by the speed of transit across the sky. A satellite may take as long as several minutes to cross the sky compared with the 3 to 4 seconds of a natural object. Apart from the speed, the general appearances are more or less the same. The recording of observations of natural fireballs applies equally to decays of satellites (see page 158).

The reporting of phenomena associated with the launching of satellites and research rockets is also of interest because the rocket exhausts can sometimes be seen from points well away from the launch site. Research rockets are launched from various sites around the world and can carry equipment for research into the environment, the upper atmosphere and for astronomical observations. They are usually projected vertically or nearly so and, after attaining their maximum height (which may be 160 km or more), fall back to the Earth's surface. The direct light from the burning propellant during the upward leg of the flight will be readily identified but some of the experiments carried by the rockets may themselves give rise to effects which are visible at night. For example, equipment may be carried which releases chemicals into the high atmosphere.

Some chemical vapours are ejected in the form of a long bright trail on the upleg or downleg of the rocket path. Night-time trails usually appear white but at twilight, about 30 minutes after sunset or before sunrise, the trails are generally yellow, red or greenish-blue. Although their size depends on the altitude at which they are released and, of course, on the position of the observer, it is not unusual for a trail to be as much as 40° long and from 1° to 5° wide. These vapour trails which may remain visible for more than 20 minutes, are generally distorted by winds in the upper atmosphere.

Sometimes 'grenades' are ejected from the rocket during the upward flight, generating acoustic waves whose reception at the ground enables the wind and temperature structure of the upper atmosphere to be calculated. At night a grenade burst would appear similar to an anti-aircraft shell burst, being much brighter than a planet but of very short duration. After 2 or 3 seconds another burst would appear displaced in the direction of flight. The number of bursts may total about 20. No sounds are likely to be heard as the acoustic waves are generated at sub-audible frequencies and are very weak in intensity on reaching the ground.

In some rocket firings the grenade ejections are extended above 100 km altitude and the gas products of the explosion then react chemically with the atmosphere, producing a faintly luminous spherical cloud about the size of the full moon although much fainter. Such clouds may last for 5 to 10 minutes before diffusing and disappearing, and during this time the wind speed and direction can be found from their drift. On other occasions a faintly luminous trail may be produced for the same purpose by the release of a certain chemical from the rocket. The trail, like the grenade clouds, is soft white in colour. Such experiments are held under twilight conditions with sunlight falling on the releases against a still dark sky. The sunlight is reradiated in certain parts of the spectrum from the cloud or trail providing a spectacular blue-green hue, or the well known yellow coloration of sodium light, if sodium vapour has been released.

THE AURORA

General

The Latin word 'aurora' means dawn, and equatorwards of the polar auroral zones a glow like a false dawn may sometimes be seen along the poleward horizon by a casual observer during the course of a dark night. 'Aurora borealis' is the name given to the phenomenon in the Northern Hemisphere and 'aurora australis', first recorded by Captain Cook in 1773, to that in the Southern Hemisphere. During a big auroral storm the glow may develop into one or more homogeneous arcs from which searchlight-like beams called rays may be emitted. The arcs may twist into rayed bands, the rays extending upwards to the zenith. At the peak of the display auroral forms may actively change location and shape while the light emitted from them may pulsate or appear like flames or flickering. As the storm subsides the rays may be superseded by diffuse patches of light without sharp borders. The whole storm may die away but there is the possibility that it will repeat itself later in the night. (Figure 25).

If the aurora is fainter than that necessary to cause colour vision the light will appear white. The normal colour usually reported is green but during intensive

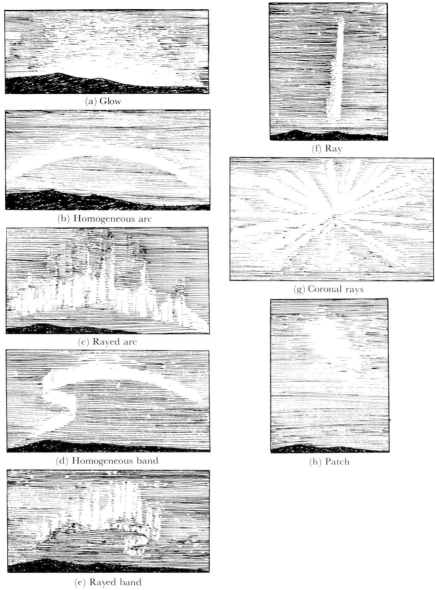

(a) Glow

(b) Homogeneous arc

(c) Rayed arc

(d) Homogeneous band

(e) Rayed band

(f) Ray

(g) Coronal rays

(h) Patch

Figure 25.   Auroral forms.

storms the bottom of an auroral arc may be tinged with red. Red rays and patches may be seen above the green structures and are associated with great height. The tops of green rays may also be tinged with red. Blue may be seen during or after big storms and if mixed with red gives a purple tinge. Rarely, white or yellow may be seen owing to the mixing of green, red and blue features.

The lower border of the aurora is usually situated at an altitude of between 90 and 120 km above the surface of the Earth. The vertical extent of the aurora varies from between a few kilometres to about 1000 km. Height is reduced with increase in brightness and there is a diurnal tidal effect. The base of the auroral arc is at about 105 km and a red tinge thereon might be as low as 90 km, or even 65 km. Red aurorae are associated with altitudes of several hundred kilometres.

The aurora is caused by the bombardment of the upper atmosphere by electrified particles either coming directly from the Sun or due to the release of particles trapped in space adjacent to the Earth by the Earth's magnetic field. The particles are guided into the atmosphere by the magnetic field lines and accelerated by the associated electric fields. The impact of particles and their reaction with the atoms and molecules of oxygen and nitrogen convert particle energy into light energy, each reaction with its own specific colour, rather like the activity present that makes a neon tube glow.

The Polar Aurora and Storm Aurora.   Around each of the Earth's magnetic poles lies an oval of auroral activity. The dayside of each oval is at about 15° of latitude from the magnetic pole and the nightside is at about 20°. The auroral zone on the Earth's surface is the locus of the ground swept by the nightside of the oval as the Earth turns beneath it. The dayside of the aurora can only be observed by ships and landsmen under the polar winter sunless sky. Certain interactions between the interplanetary and the Earth's magnetic fields can produce a westward surge in the nightside auroral oval activity followed by a retreat polewards. This is known as an auroral substorm. Other magnetic and particle reactions between interplanetary space and the Earth produce a full-blown magnetic storm when the auroral oval expands equatorwards into mid latitudes, and in extreme cases produces visible aurora in the Tropics such as on March 13 1989, when a number of ships observed activity in the Caribbean Sea, and in the Indian Ocean from the Cape of Good Hope to Madagascar.

Visual Observation of the Aurora

Observation of the aurora need not involve any particularly specialized equipment. The position of auroral forms is best described in terms of true azimuth and to angular altitudes above the horizon, rather than relative to the positions of visible stars. To this end a sextant is helpful with angles measured to the nearest degree, especially when measuring the altitude of the lowest edge of any arc present. For observers without instruments to hand an outstretched handspan from thumb to little finger approximates to 20° and the knuckles, like the handspan held at arm's length, approximate to 2°.

It is particularly important to record the UTC date and time, and the ship's position when an aurora is seen. The simplest record of an observation is to make a written description of what is seen, including forms, their location, colours and changes with time. The notes may be enhanced by making a series of sketches to scale, adding notes on colour, azimuth and altitude, brightness, obstructing cloud or other phenomena. Artistic skill is not called for but many mariners succeed in producing praiseworthy efforts. Some observers draw a circle to represent the horizon with the centre as the astronomical zenith and make a drawing equivalent to photography made with a fisheye lens. Note that visual observers tend to overestimate the brightness of auroral forms.

A more detailed record of an active storm is effected by making use of the International Aurora Code and the standard form used for this purpose. Copies of the Code and Report Form are given in Appendix II. An observer would make an entry on the form at about once every 5 minutes or at every change in the appearance and activity of the aurora. There is space on the form for sketches to amplify the report, for an active display may be such that the rate of change may be faster than the observer can fill in the form and he has to make judgements as to the time and nature of the major changes in the apparition. Details of the sky condition and interference to visibility due to cloud, haze, moonlight, precipitation and the like should be noted. Any unusual radar images, distortion or loss of radio signals on HF or long distance VHF reception are worth recording, with the bearing of the incoming signal, when possible.

The observer should note particularly if rays on the horizon appear to fan out like spokes of a wheel from a hub apparently below the horizon or if they stand vertical or appear to converge towards a hub point above the horizon. Note particularly the times when aurora is overhead, either as bands, coronal converging rays or spirals. Be aware that during a strong auroral storm, in higher latitudes such as the Norwegian Sea, the auroral oval may have swept equatorwards to the extent that the aurora is on the equatorward and not the poleward side of the ship, an all round check of the sky being necessary.

Photography of Aurora
Unless anchored or moored alongside, in calm waters a ship does not present a very stable base for time exposure photography, but this has been successfully carried out, both from ships at sea and aircraft overflying Canada. Any camera with a lens ratio of f2.8 or faster can be used. Film may be colour or black-and-white but some makes have a better colour balance and grain structure than others. Film speeds of ISO 200 to 400 are normal but high speeds of 1000 have been used. Speeds of ISO 100 having suitable properties for aurora work are available.

Depending upon the brightness of the aurora, exposure times of between 5 and 30 seconds may be required. Longer exposures may suffer from fogging by nearby urban lighting or moonlight and star images will start to trail across the photograph, but 60-second exposures have been used on faint quiet aurora with slow film. If unsure of the exposure required it is best to take a number of photographs in quick succession using progressively longer exposures, say from 10 to 30 seconds. Most beginners tend to overexpose, especially with faint aurorae, and background light tends to fog the picture. Colour photography is useful in detecting the various hues and their locations that might not be visible to the naked eye, such as the red lower fringe of a strong rayed arc.

Observers on board ships of the UK Voluntary Observing Fleet may enter the details of auroral sightings in the meteorological logbook making use of the recording methods described above. On receipt of the logs at the Met. Office the information is extracted and copies used by aurora researchers. Copies of the log entries are also sent to the University of Aberdeen for storage with the existing Balfour Stewart Auroral Laboratory and other national auroral records.

METEORS AND FIREBALLS

During the night watches the seaman has many opportunities for obtaining useful observations of meteors. The general term used to refer to all the small bodies orbiting the Sun between the planets is 'meteoroid', and from a point on the surface of the Earth their presence is recorded only when they approach too closely to the Earth and enter the upper regions of the atmosphere, when they become incandescent due to the heat generated by friction between the body and the molecules (and atoms) of the atmosphere. They are then referred to as 'meteors' and appear as luminous streaks in the sky, popularly known as 'shooting stars'. They have of course no connection with any star, being usually small fragments varying in size from a grain of sand up to a pea. It is estimated that many thousands of millions of these objects enter the atmosphere daily, but all except a minute fraction of them are much too faint to be seen by the naked eye. The vast majority of all meteors are entirely disintegrated and subsequently settle down slowly to the Earth's surface in the form of extremely fine dust. In general the brightness of a meteor depends on two factors, the size of the object and the speed at which it enters the atmosphere. The greater the speed the brighter the object.

Larger objects generate much more light and if the intensity of this light rivals or surpasses the brightness of the planets, and in particular the planet Venus, they are referred to as 'fireballs'. This is an unfortunate term as it is also sometimes used to describe ball lightning. If the light rivals that of the full moon or brighter they are often called 'major fireballs'. Some rival the Sun in brilliance but these are relatively rare. The majority of the objects producing fireballs are completely disintegrated high up in the upper regions of the atmosphere but some survive the atmospheric passage and reach the Earth's surface. These objects are called 'meteorites'. Meteorite falls are relatively rare but observational reports of such an event are of great importance.

Appearance and speed of meteors. The appearance and speed of meteors and fireballs is as varied as their brightness. Some travel quickly, others slowly. The apparent path across the sky is usually a straight line or arc, but it may take other forms. Some leave streaks of sparks or luminous vapour known as trains and also dust trails. In many cases the trail disappears immediately but in others it can remain visible for seconds or minutes, or in rare cases for periods up to two hours. In such cases, changes may be observed in it, these changes being caused by winds in the upper atmosphere, combined with the fall of the material due to gravity. Most bright meteors and fireballs are brightly coloured, with red and green being the most common colours, but often the distribution of the colours can change during the flight. Sometimes the fireball appears to break up with the detached portions then proceeding separately, or it may explode at the end of its visible track. The trains are often reddish, white or golden, reflecting the coloration of the object itself. A common reported event is the appearance of a red fireball travelling slowly across the sky and hitting the surface of the Earth. This is an optical illusion. The eye cannot by itself estimate accurately distance, and range is recorded by the brain in terms of the brightness of the object. The brighter the object, the nearer it appears to be. There is no foundation to this. As an example, the planet Venus, when low in the sky near the horizon, is often mistaken for an atmospheric object, simply because it can be very bright. In the case of the red fireball it is simply that it is passing over the horizon but still many tens of kilometres up in the atmosphere. As a general rule for objects of average size which do produce meteorites, they will have slowed up sufficiently during their atmospheric passage to have cooled down and therefore become invisible before they reach the surface.

The duration of a meteor's flight is rarely more than 3 seconds, and is often greatly overestimated. The theoretical range of speeds for objects entering the atmosphere is from 11–70 km per second but the majority lie within the approximate range of 15–50 km per second. The average height above the Earth's surface is 120–130 km at the time of appearance, to 70–80 km at the time of disappearance, but some bright fireballs can penetrate much lower than this before burning out. The height of the beginning and end of a meteor's visible path in the atmosphere and its speed are determined by observations made by two observers some distance apart, up to 100 n.mile or more. At much greater distances the same meteor could not be seen by both observers, since an individual meteor is only visible over a small part of the Earth's surface and would thus be below the horizon of one of the observers. In this joint observation each observer notes the points of appearance and disappearance of the meteor in the sky as accurately as possible, and the duration of its flight. The information derived from such observations is valuable, not only in extending our knowledge of meteors, but also in making inferences about the temperature of the attenuated atmosphere at very great heights above the Earth's surface.

Frequency of meteors. Meteor showers. The number of meteors seen in a given time is usually greater on nights of higher atmospheric transparency, since more of the fainter meteors are seen and these are much more numerous than the brighter ones. On nights of equal clarity, about twice as many are visible in July to December as in January to June. Furthermore, on any single night of the year, the hourly rate of meteor appearance is greater after local midnight than before it. These remarks refer to average conditions and the numbers actually seen can vary considerably. On certain nights the number of meteors seen is far more numerous than expected and a high proportion of the tracks when produced backwards seem to converge from the same point or small area in the sky. This point is called a radiant and such a group of meteors with the same radiant belong to the same meteor shower. Each of these showers is given a name, with the letters -id(s) added to the name of the constellation in which the radiant is situated. For example, the active meteor shower seen in August and having a radiant in the constellation Perseus is referred to as the Perseid shower, or just the Perseids. Many of these showers are active each year but not necessarily with the same intensity. Some are highly active at intervals of a few years. For example the Leonids in November give a display of many thousand meteors per hour at roughly 33-year intervals. The particles producing a meteor shower were moving in the same general orbit round the Sun and the meteors are seen at times when the Earth is at, or near to, the point of intersection of this orbit with the Earth's orbit round the Sun. In a few cases the orbit of the shower has been found to be the same as that of a known comet, of whose material the meteors originally formed a part. For example, the Orionids, seen in October, are associated with Comet Halley.

Meteorites

Very bright fireballs with intensities rivalling that of the full moon, consist mainly of two types. The most common, comprising a high percentage of the fireballs seen, consist of possibly a loose agglomeration of small particles and in most cases they are completely burned up during the passage through the atmosphere. A small percentage, however, comprise a solid lump of rock, and although a high percentage of this rock will be ablated during its passage through the atmosphere, the remainder could reach the Earth's surface and are called meteorites.

If the meteorite is large enough it could form a crater, the form of which being dependent on mass and the velocity of impact. For small meteorites the last part of the track through the atmosphere cannot be seen because it has lost most of its cosmic velocity and hence cooled down, losing its glow in the process. It is therefore exceptionally rare for a meteorite to be seen to land. If the splash and related phenomena are seen at sea, full details should be recorded. Before the object reaches the Earth's surface, it will be travelling supersonically and the sonic boom will be heard over a wide area. The recording of a sonic boom is a good indication of the fall of a meteorite, especially if a brilliant fireball is observed. Logging of such events should be made in the greatest possible detail.

PRINCIPAL METEOR STREAMS*

Shower	Maxima	*Date* Normal Limits	Notes
Quadrantids	Jan 3/4	Jan 1–6	Blue meteors. Fine trains.
Virginids	Apr 12	Mar–Apr	Slow, long paths.
Lyrids	Apr 22	Apr 19–25	
η-Aquarids	May 5	Apr 24–May 20	Fine southern hemisphere shower.
α-Scorpids	Apr 28	Apr 20–May 19	Part of the Scorpio-Sagittariid
	May 13		complex, with several radiants.
Ophiuchids	Jun 10	May 19–July	Several radiants.
	Jun 20		
α-Cygnids	Jul 21	July–August	One of a number of radiants active
	Aug 21		in northern summer months.
Capricornids	Jul 8	July–August	Bright meteors. May have three
	Jul 15		maxima and multiple radiant.
	Jul 26		
δ-Aquarids	Jul 29	Jul 15–Aug 20	Fine southern shower with a double
	Aug 7		radiant. Meteors tend to be faint.
Piscis-Australids	Jul 31	Jul 15–Aug 20	
α-Capricornids	Aug 2	Jul 15–Aug 25	Slow yellow fireballs.
ι-Aquarids	Aug 7	July–August	Faint meteors.
Perseids	Aug 12/13	Jul 23–Aug 20	Bright fast moving meteors, many trained.
Piscids	Sep 9	Sept–October	Multi-radiant.
	Sep 21		
	Oct 13		
Orionids	Oct 22	Oct 16–27	Fast moving with fine trains.
Taurids	Nov 4	Oct 20–Nov 30	Very slow moving meteors.
Leonids	Nov 17/18	Nov 15–20	Swift bright meteors with fine trains.
Puppids-Velids	Dec 9	Nov 27–January	
	Dec 26		
Geminids	Dec 14	Dec 7–16	Bright meteors, moderate speed.
Ursids	Dec 23	Dec 17–25	

*Reproduced by courtesy of the British Astronomical Association.

Recording of observations of meteors and fireballs
Because of the suddenness of the occurrence of such events, it is usually difficult to record a full account, the following notes being given as guidance to the kind of useful information desired by those analysing this type of phenomenon.

1. The positions of the points of appearance and disappearance in the sky. These can be given with reference to the star background or in the form of azimuth and altitude. If the end points are not observed, any positional data will be of value. Records of the azimuth and altitude when the object was highest in the sky will also be of value.
2. The date and time of the event and the duration of the flight in seconds.
3. Details of the physical appearance, brightness, colour, changes in brightness and colour, fragmentation (if it occurs), existence of a train and/or a dust trail.
4. Any interesting or unusual phenomena seen during the passage across the sky. Of importance, the recording of a sonic boom, which may be heard as much as two minutes after the visible passage, is of exceptional interest.

It must be mentioned that although the observer may be at sea, the track of the fireball may pass over land and so the marine observations could provide details of a section of the flight poorly recorded from land positions.

NOCTILUCENT CLOUDS

These beautiful ice-crystal 'clouds' occur under the mesopause at a height of about 83 km where the barometric pressure is only one hundred thousandth of the sea level value, and the temperatures are the lowest in the atmosphere, some $-130°$ to -160 °C. Under these conditions ice crystals grow from the very small amounts of water vapour present, to form thin tenuous clouds which have a superficial resemblance to cirrus or cirrocumulus.

Noctilucent clouds (NLC) are normally seen in summer in fairly high latitudes, and when the sun is between about 6° and 16° below the horizon. They cannot be seen in daylight but appear when the sky is sufficiently dark, in the twilight arch, shining brightly with a pearly-white or electric-blue radiance, sometimes golden or greenish when near the horizon. However, when NLC is overhead it is very faint and difficult to distinguish from cirrus lit by the twilight glow or the moon. When the sun is sufficiently far below the horizon, the much lower clouds of the troposphere are no longer illuminated and appear as black silhouettes, but the NLC shines out in the darkening sky. In the northern hemisphere NLC are usually seen between about the end of May to about mid-August, with a peak around the first week of July. They are seldom seen below latitude 50°, and in Arctic regions their visibility is limited by the brightness of the midnight sky near the solstice. In the Southern Hemisphere there are few observers at such latitudes, but NLC have been observed from the Falkland Islands and the Antarctic, and more observations are needed from this region. (See photograph on page 92.)

Interest in noctilucent clouds is growing. Studies of them are helping our understanding of the movements and physical processes of the upper atmosphere, and there is some evidence that they are on the increase. Data on NLC are much needed by upper-air physicists, and it is desirable to have as many observers as possible, spread over a wide area, for a greater chance of NLC occurrences to be seen and logged. It is important to note not only 'positive' but also 'negative' nights, i.e. those nights in summer above about latitude 54° with a clear or nearly clear sky during which no NLC is seen over the observing period; it must be remembered that NLC which is only just visible to the naked eye is easily visible with binoculars. Unlike aurorae, NLC change in shape very slowly during a night, and observations should if possible be made at 15-minute intervals, i.e. on the hour and the quarter-hours and so on. Sketches can be very useful, photographs more so; but on a moving ship the requisite long exposures make this impracticable. For an observer on a stable platform a 200 ISO colour film, and exposure of 5 to 8 seconds at f2.8 should give good results. A note should be made of the time any photograph is taken, and a full report should include:

(a) **Place** of observation with latitude and longitude to the nearest half-degree.
(b) **Time** in UTC.
(c) **Date**, using the double-date system employed with aurorae, e.g. June 23/24 means the night of the 23rd and the early morning of the 24th.
(d) **Observing conditions.** These should be described briefly, e.g. mist, patchy cloud, bright moon.
(e) **Elevation.** If possible, measure the maximum altitude of the upper border of the display.
(f) **Azimuth.** If NLC is present, the left-hand and right-hand azimuths of the total display should be observed: it is not necessary to measure individual parts of the display.
(g) **Brightness.** If the NLC is faint or only visible with binoculars, log '1', if intensely bright log '3', otherwise log '2'.
(h) **Structure.** The following standard cloud types are used in the Observation Manual of the World Meteorological Organization. They can occur in any or all combinations:

TYPE I. Veils. Very tenuous, lacking in structure, usually faint, often as a 'background' to other forms.
TYPE II. Bands. Long streaks, often in groups, parallel to each other or crossing at small angles.
TYPE III. Billows. Closely spaced, resembling waves or ripples, the herring-bone structure being characteristic of NLC but not always observed.
TYPE IV. Whirls. Large-scale looped structures, often as complete or partial rings.
TYPE V. Amorphous. Similar to veils in the lack of structure but brighter and usually in patches.

The simultaneous occurrence of NLC and aurora is very unusual and is of great theoretical interest because the connection between the two phenomena is not fully understood. Observers should describe changes in both phenomena in detail, e.g. appearance and disappearance times, sudden brightenings and other obvious features.

CHAPTER 11

PHENOMENA OF THE LOWER ATMOSPHERE

The presence of water droplets, ice crystals and dust particles in the atmosphere and local abnormalities in the distribution of temperature and humidity give rise to a wide variety of interesting and beautiful phenomena which are mainly due to either the reflection, refraction or scattering of the rays of the sun or moon. Many of these 'optical phenomena' are described below. Also included are descriptions of a few phenomena which are due to other causes and which are equally worthy of careful observation when they occur.

ABNORMAL REFRACTION AND MIRAGE

A mirage is produced by refraction and/or reflection of light in the layers of air close to the Earth's surface. Two main classes of mirage occur, (a) inferior and (b) superior, in which the virtual image is below and above the object, respectively. The inferior image is seen over a flat, strongly heated surface (e.g. desert) and gives the illusion of an expanse of water if it reflects the sky. A superior mirage is seen in the sky at low altitude where a temperature inversion forms a discontinuity between air at different temperatures. Light from an object is, in this case, reflected off the discontinuity. Such mirages can also show multiple images, the upright ones being caused by refraction through discontinuity. Mirages can also involve magnification (in one or two directions).

Mention should be made of the Novaya Zemlya mirage, a phenomenon in which an astronomical body is seen to rise or set when it is in fact well below the horizon. It can be caused by sighting across a cold ocean or ice expanse, where the surface is much colder than the air above it. It can also be caused by a discontinuity forming in the upper atmosphere over a very wide area.

Good descriptions and sketches of the various forms of mirage and the effects of abnormal refraction are always of interest, especially of the more striking forms, such as a well-developed superior mirage. Unusual phenomena should be carefully reported, such as the apparent discontinuity of distortion of the horizon line that has been occasionally seen, also lateral mirages and the complicated mixed mirages of the Strait of Messina, known by the name, of Italian origin, of 'fata morgana'. When lights are seen at abnormal distances, the normal distance of visibility should

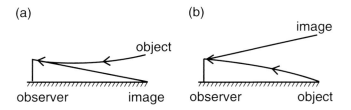

Figure 26.   Mirages. (a) Inferior image, (b) Superior image.

be given. In all observations of abnormal refraction and mirage, the temperature of air and sea, the type and amount of cloud present, and the direction and force of the wind should be noted.

Photography may be helpful in resolving controversial questions such as that of the possibility of lateral mirage in the free atmosphere and that of mirage magnifying (or diminishing) laterally and vertically simultaneously. It is particularly useful if the characteristics of the camera and its lens system, and also in the latter case those (distance and dimensions) of the objects whose mirage images are observed, are known and logged.

GLORY OR BROCKEN SPECTRE

In a foggy atmosphere an observer, standing with his back to the sun, when this is at low altitude, will sometimes see the shadow of himself, or of his head, thrown upon the fog, together with coloured rings of light surrounding the shadow. The phenomenon was first noted on the Brocken mountain in Germany but it is not confined to mountain districts and it is most common in Arctic regions, where it is seen on every occasion of simultaneous sunshine and fog.

The coloured rings are now usually known as a 'glory'. A typical series of colours seen in a well-developed one is as follows. There is a general whitish-yellow colour round the shadow, surrounded by rings of colour in order outwards: dull red, bluish-green, reddish-violet, blue, green, red, green, red. A white rainbow at a considerable distance outside the glory is sometimes also seen.

The shadow of the observer on thick fog may be seen at night if there is a bright artificial light behind him.

COLOURED SUNS AND MOONS

The various red or orange colours ordinarily exhibited by the sun, moon and some other astronomical bodies when near the horizon are generally caused by these bodies being viewed through a great thickness of the dust-laden lower atmosphere, which absorbs most of the sunlight of shorter wavelengths, leaving the longer ones, mainly yellow and red, to come through.

Occasionally at twilight the moon appears to be of a greenish colour, usually a pale greenish-blue or a pale apple-green colour. This is an effect of colour contrast when the twilight hues of the surrounding sky are brighter than usual, either purplish or reddish, or when the moon is near or covered by thin, brightly tinted cloud.

Coloured suns or moons, not an effect of colour contrast, are sometimes seen. This phenomenon may be produced by dust or smoke haze in the lower atmosphere, e.g. a scirocco laden with dust from the Sahara may give a blue sun or moon in the Mediterranean, and a similar colour may be given in the region of extensive bush fires. The phenomenon may also be produced by volcanic dust at high atmospheric levels. Blue and green moons were observed on many occasions after the great eruption of Krakatoa in 1883 and the sun assumed many different and often quite brilliant colours. Shades of red and copper, green, golden-green, blue, both silvery and leaden, were seen on various days in different localities.

Coloured suns and moons were seen over much of western Europe between 26 and 30 September 1950. These were produced by the smoke from an extensive forest fire in Alberta, Canada which began on 23 September. The sun's colour was observed in different places as steel-grey, deep blue and purple.

Any observations of this kind are of interest.

CORONAE

A corona consists of one or more coloured rings round the sun or moon as centre, when either of these bodies is covered with middle or lower cloud thin enough to allow the greater part of the light to come through. It is distinguished from a halo by its smaller size and different colouring, as explained below. A fully developed corona shows a bluish-white or yellowish glow, usually 2° or 3° in diameter, round the sun (or moon). Outside this is a brownish-red ring. The inner glow and the brownish ring together constitute what is called the aureole. Outside this are coloured rings, in the opposite colour sequence to that of a halo, namely violet or blue nearest the sun and red farthest out. Sometimes the whole of this colour sequence is repeated outwards a second or, on rare occasions, even a third or fourth time. A corona showing the outer coloured rings is comparatively infrequent, but the aureole alone is the commonest of optical meteorological phenomena and is formed, at any rate partially, whenever broken cloud edges of cumulus, stratus or stratocumulus pass over the sun or moon.

While the radii of the various haloes are constant, that of a corona varies on different occasions, being dependent on the size of the water drops in the cloud. The outside radius of a fully developed corona is usually much smaller than that of the 22° halo, and is generally between 5° and 8°. After great volcanic eruptions, when fine dust is suspended at great heights in the atmosphere, an aureole comparable in size with the 22° halo has been seen; it is known as Bishop's ring.

If the drop size varies from place to place in the cloud the corona will have an irregular circumference, this being the transition to 'iridescent cloud' (see below), with completely irregular patches of rainbow colour.

Faint coronae are visible round the bright planets, Venus and Jupiter, and also Mars when this is sufficiently bright, providing the cloud is very thin. They may sometimes be seen round the brightest stars, especially if binoculars are used.

A yellowish blur 2° or 3° in diameter is often seen round the sun or moon and is sometimes formed by higher cloud than that which normally gives coronae. Although it has a fairly sharply defined circular edge it must not be regarded as an aureole unless bounded by the characteristic brownish-red ring.

In certain circumstances the sun or moon may show a halo and a corona simultaneously.

The name 'corona' is also given to the outer part of the sun's atmosphere (see page 144); this is directly visible only during a solar eclipse and is distinguished by the term 'solar corona'.

CORPOSANT

The electrical phenomenon known as Corposant or St Elmo's Fire is not infrequently observed at sea during squalls and thunderstorms. It is a luminous apparition seen at the extremities of masts and sometimes on the stays, aerial, jackstaff or other parts of the ship. It may appear as a brush discharge of radiating streamers several inches long, or as luminous globes, a number of which are sometimes seen along the aerial. At other times a structureless glow envelops an elongated object, such as a mast or an aerial. St Elmo's Fire is usually bluish or greenish in colour, but a violet glow has been reported and sometimes the colour is pure white.

CREPUSCULAR RAYS

The word 'crepuscular' means 'associated with twilight'. Occasionally, soon after sunset, the clear sky appears to be divided into lighter and darker rays by lines diverging from the position of the sun below the horizon. The lighter rays are those illuminated by sunshine; they are usually coloured pink, but may, on different occasions, show some shade of red or orange. The darker rays are shadows, from which the sunlight is cut off by clouds near or just below the horizon or by the irregularities of hills and mountains on the horizon. They appear greenish by contrast with pink rays. (See photographs on page 93.)

As the light rays come from the sun, and so are practically parallel, their apparent divergence is an effect of perspective. In favourable circumstances the light rays and shadows extend right across the sky and appear to converge, by perspective, to a point a little above the eastern horizon. These 'anti-crepuscular rays' are generally ill defined.

It is not necessary to record this phenomenon in the logbook unless it shows some feature of special interest, such as unusually distinct colouring or a well-defined convergence to the eastern horizon.

On rare occasions one or more bands have been seen extending up into the sky, from the western horizon, at a later stage of twilight. They appear of a deep blue colour, darker than the general blue of the sky, and are probably shadows of mountains well below the horizon. It is of interest to record these observations.

There are two other allied phenomena which are frequently seen and are of no special interest, unless some unusual feature is observed. The first consists of pale blue or whitish rays diverging from the sun in the daytime when it is behind cumulus or cumulonimbus cloud. The rays are sharply defined and separated by deep blue bands, which are the shadows of parts of the irregular cloud edge. The second is associated with stratus or other cloud obscuring the sun. If there are small gaps in the cloud, sunbeams pierce these, directed more or less downwards, and are rendered luminous by mist or dust in the air. This is popularly known as 'the sun drawing water'.

DUSTFALL AT SEA

Dust from the land may be blown over the adjacent sea by high winds, but not normally in appreciable quantity. In special regions, e.g. the Red Sea, sand- or dust-storms are not infrequent and are sometimes severe.

Desert dust or sand may be carried up to high levels of the atmosphere and finally be dispersed over so great an area as not to form any perceptible deposit on falling. The desert dust from Australia carried north-westward by the south-east monsoon reduces visibility over the East Indies region but is not observed as dustfall.

On the other hand, falls of fine reddish or brownish dust from the Sahara, carried by the trade wind, are experienced over a large area of the eastern North Atlantic adjacent to the coast of Africa, centred roughly on Cape Verde Islands. At times this deposit may lie quite thickly on board ship. Visibility in this area is often poor; not infrequently the sun appears blood-red and at night all but the brightest stars at high altitudes are obscured.

Examples of dustfall. Considerable or heavy dustfall may be experienced after a great volcanic eruption. Dust from the eruption of Krakatoa in 1883 was collected on board ship in the Indian Ocean at a distance of 1000 nautical miles. After the eruption of Hekla in March 1947, dust was similarly collected at a distance of 450 n.mile. In August 1966 the dust from the eruption of Mount Awu in the Sangihe Islands covered the decks of a ship 225 miles away in the Celebes Sea.

In more recent times, volcanic dust from the eruption of Mount Pinatubo in the Philippines in June 1991 was collected on board m.v. *British Skill* when more than 450 n.mile south-west of the volcano's position; and after the eruption of Mount Hudson in Chile on 17 August 1991, m.v. *Remuera Bay* experienced a grey-green haze and heavy dustfall when passing west of the Falkland Islands nine days after the eruption and more than 500 n.mile distant from the volcano.

THE GREEN FLASH

At sunset, the small segment of the upper part of the sun's disc, which is the last to disappear, may turn emerald-green or bluish-green at the instant of its setting. The phenomenon thus usually lasts only a fraction of a second, which is the reason for calling it the 'green flash', but longer durations of the colour are occasionally seen.

Sun. The green flash is not always seen and when it is seen it is not always equally brilliant. It can range from a green of extreme brilliance and purity, conspicuous without optical aid, down to a trace of grey-green coloration observable only with binoculars.

The green flash is produced by the last rays of sunlight emanating from the upper limb of the sun, at sunset, being refracted before reaching the observer's eye. The shorter waves which appear as violet, blue and green light suffer greater refraction than the orange and red longer waves of the white sunlight. The fringes of the upper limb cannot usually be seen while the main body of the sun is still above the horizon, as the general sunlight is too strong, but when most of this is cut off by the horizon they spring suddenly into view. Normally, only the green fringe is seen, the light of still shorter wavelengths usually being scattered by its horizontal passage through the lower atmosphere. The flash is, however, occasionally seen as a blue one, or as green quickly changing to blue. On very rare occasions the violet colour has been seen.

The green colour occasionally appears in other ways. Sometimes when refraction is marked, and the sun's disc is perhaps distorted, the use of shaded binoculars will show that the upper limb appears to be 'boiling', giving off shreds or tongues of green 'vapour'. Occasionally the sun's upper limb has been seen with a narrow green rim when half or more of the disc remained above the horizon.

A sea horizon is not essential for observing the green flash; it may be equally well seen when the sun sets behind a distant land surface. It has also often been seen when the upper limb sinks below a bank of hard-edged cloud at low altitude, and if there are several parallel bars of cloud in clear sky the phenomenon may be seen more than once on the same evening. When the lower line of the sun appears from behind cloud near the horizon the converse phenomenon, the 'red flash', has sometimes been seen.

Moon and planets. The green flash occurs also with the moon, but has seldom been observed, presumably because it is fainter and rarely looked for. On the other hand, it has been frequently seen at the setting of the bright planets Venus and Jupiter, and an observation of a blue flash from Venus is on record. Many interesting varieties of phenomena may occur before these planets set, the observation usually requiring binoculars. Colour changes may be seen, usually between white, red and green, or two images may appear of the same or different colours. The planet may exhibit slow 'shimmering' movements, obviously due to abnormal refraction.

Observing conditions. The most favourable conditions for seeing the green flash, at any rate brilliantly, is probably some degree of abnormal refraction, whereby the vertical extent of the colour separation described above is greater than that produced by normal refraction. In addition, the green flash is most likely to be seen when the air is relatively dust-free, and without mist or haze, so that the sun remains brighter and less red than usual at low altitudes. The green flash has been well observed at sunrise, but less frequently, perhaps because it is less often looked for. Also, owing to its short duration the phenomenon is liable to be missed unless the exact spot at which the sun will appear is known.

The green flash has sometimes been called, rather inappropriately, the 'green ray'. It will be obvious from the remarks made above that it exhibits a considerable variety of appearances at different times. Further observations, giving as much detail as possible, will be very useful in increasing our knowledge of the interesting phenomenon and the conditions most favourable for its appearance.

Other green phenomena

Other phenomena involving green coloration of the sky in the vicinity of the sun at the moment of sunset are occasionally seen, and observations of these are also of interest, as they exhibit much variety. Some examples are (a) a momentary ray of green light shooting up into the sky, sometimes to a considerable altitude at, or just before, the final instant of sunset, (b) an appearance resembling a rapidly rotating green searchlight beam, (c) a transitory appearance as of green mist in the sky above the setting sun.

HALO PHENOMENA

Halo phenomena

A group of optical phenomena in the form of rings, arcs, pillars or bright spots, produced by refraction or reflection of light by ice crystals suspended in the atmosphere (cirriform clouds, ice fog, etc.).

These phenomena may show colours when formed by refraction of the light from the sun, but the rarer halo phenomena produced by the light of the moon are usually white. For convenience the source is usually referred to as the Sun. The many different kinds of halo which have been observed may be described by reference to Figure 27. This is a composite diagram made up from a number of drawings of an unusually complete halo display seen at about midday on 6 March 1941 in various localities in the west Midlands.

The four rings described below (three haloes and the parhelic circle) may, under very favourable conditions, appear complete but they are more frequently incomplete. Parts of these rings, together with the arcs and mock suns described on pages 169–175, may at times be seen with no apparent connection with one another; the sky may then assume a very strange appearance.

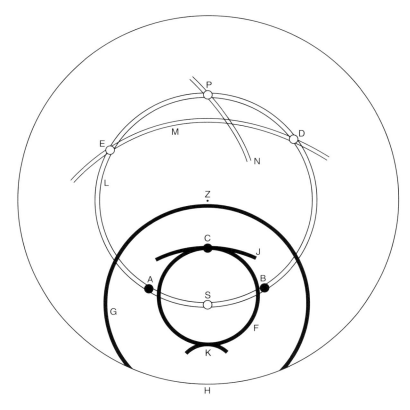

Figure 27.   Halo phenomena.

An unusually complete halo display observed at about midday on 6 March 1941 in the west Midlands; composite diagram based on observations from various localities. Appearances due to refraction, which may be brilliantly coloured, as on this occasion, are shown black; appearances due to reflection, which are always white, are shown by the finer lines. The outer circle, H, is the complete horizon, with Z, the zenith, in the centre; S is the Sun, P the anthelion, A, B, C, D and E are parhelia or mock suns; F is the 22° halo, G the 46° halo; J and K are upper and lower arcs of contact of F; L is the parhelic circle or mock-sun ring (parallel to the horizon), M the arc through the mock suns at 120° (usually a pair of arcs not joined in the middle), and N the oblique arc through P (one of a symmetrical pair which may sometimes be seen together).

168

The halo phenomena predicted by standard theory are symmetrical about the solar vertical, apart from possible suppression in certain parts of the sky by the absence of suitable crystals in that direction. Certain very rare exceptions are apparently due to orientation of crystal axes in a direction somewhat tilted from the vertical.

Halo of 22° (small halo)
This is the most frequent halo phenomenon and appears as a luminous ring, F, in the figure, with the sun or moon, S, as centre, and having a radius of 22°. The space within the ring appears less bright than that just outside. The ring, if faint, is white; when more strongly developed it shows coloration; the edge nearest the sun is red and this is followed by yellow and, in some rare cases, a green or violet fringe can be detected on the outside.

The angle of 22° is the angle of minimum deviation for light passing through a prism of ice with faces inclined at 60°, and this halo is probably due to the refraction of light through hexagonal prisms among ice crystals in cloud.

Arcs of contact to 22° halo
Among the phenomena which, from their manner of information, can be seen only as arcs, are the so-called arcs of contact. Two of these are shown in Figure 27 — an arc of upper contact, J, and an arc of lower contact, K. The arc of lower contact is rarer than the upper, and contact arcs which occasionally appear at the sides of the halo are very rare.

When the sun is low the arcs of upper contact appear with their convex sides turned towards the sun. The points of contact with the halo are brightest, and sometimes all that is to be seen of these arcs are local brightenings of the halo at these points.

When the sun is high the arcs of upper and lower contact may appear concave to the sun. Occasionally at these higher solar elevations, the ends of the arcs are joined to form a circumscribed halo which is approximately elliptical when the sun is high enough. Other arcs, somewhat similar to the arcs of contact, but for most solar elevations standing just a little further out from the sun, and convex or concave to it, are occasionally seen. These are called Parry arcs, and there are generally two types above, two below, the sun.

Parhelic circle (the mock-sun ring) and the parhelia ('mock suns' or 'sun dogs')
A number of halo phenomena are to be observed on a circle centred on the zenith and passing through the sun. It is evident that, the higher the sun, the smaller is this circle, and that when the sun is very low, the circle appears as very nearly straight (that is, as part of a great circle), and parallel to the horizon.

Occasionally the whole circle appears as a white ring, the horizontal or parhelic circle or mock-sun ring, or substantial portions of such may be seen. The commonest phenomena on the circle, however, are the parhelia, mock suns, or sun dogs, sometimes distinguished as the parhelia of 22°. With low sun, these bright spots stand on the halo of 22°, but they gradually move out slightly as the solar elevation increases, and for very high sun cannot be seen at all. They can be very luminous, especially at low sun, and of brilliant colours, especially at rather higher sun when these parhelia are smaller. Even with low sun, the red, on the side nearest the sun, is prominent. Sometimes most notably when the sun is moderately low the parhelia have whitish tails, extending some way, outwards only (that is away from the sun), along the parhelic circle.

Other lightspots occasionally seen on the parhelic circle are the white anthelion or counter-sun at 180° azimuth from the sun, and perhaps slightly commoner are at least one kind of 'paranthelia' lying between the parhelia of 22° and the anthelion. Of the paranthelia, the best attested are the white parhelia of 120°, standing at this azimuth from the sun, though there seem to be other, rarer classes (coloured according to theory).

The corresponding phenomena produced by the moon are called 'paraselenic circle', 'paraselenae', 'parantiselenae' and the 'antiselene': the last three can be called 'mock moons'.

Various arcs are to be seen crossing the parhelic circle, often obliquely, at all these lightspots. Those at the parhelia of 22° are the lateral tangents arcs, already described, of the halo of that radius. For certain modes of tipping of the crystals there may be several of these. The best attested are the Arcs of Lowitz sloping down from the parhelia of 22° to contact with the 22° halo. Occasional observations of parhelia tilted in this sense at higher solar elevations may perhaps be incipient forms of some of these arcs.

There may be more than one kind of paranthelic arc (through a paranthelion). Since there is overall symmetry about the solar, and hence also about the anthelic, vertical, the very rare anthelic arcs generally occur as pairs of mirror-image oblique arcs crossing at the anthelics. Many such arc-pairs are theoretically possible, and at least two pairs of anthelic arcs have been seen simultaneously. Occasionally looped extensions, passing a good way across the sky, have been seen to link the two arms of a pair. In theory, some anthelic arcs may be coloured in regions remote from the anthelion. Similar white arcs, the heliac arcs, have on very rare occasions been seen intersecting at the sun.

Sun pillars

These are fairly common, at any rate at sunrise and sunset. They generally taper upwards, sometimes to at least 20° above the sun. At sunset they may be entirely red, but usually they are white, occasionally blindingly so, and on rare occasions may show a marked glittering effect.

The undersun

This is a halo phenomenon produced by reflection of sunlight on ice crystals in clouds. It appears vertically below the sun in the form of a brilliant white spot, similar to the image of the sun on a calm water surface. It is necessary to look downward to see the undersun; the phenomenon is therefore only observed from aircraft or from mountains.

The halo of 46° and related arcs

Another whole class of halo phenomena similar to that comprising the 22° halo, parhelia, arcs of contact and Parry arcs, but rarer, is to be observed at an angular distance of 46°, or a little more, from the sun. These phenomena require crystals with faces at right angles. The true halo of 46° is rare, and indeed its real existence has been doubted. Many observations claimed as being of such may actually be of its supralateral tangent arc (see below).

The least controversial of this group of phenomena are the upper and lower circumzenithal arcs (also sometimes called respectively simply 'the circumzenithal arc' and 'the circumhorizontal arc' respectively): they appear to lie in horizontal planes, like the parhelic circle.

The upper circumzenithal arc (brightly coloured, with red on the outside and violet on the inside) is a rather sharply curved arc of a small horizontal circle near the zenith; the lower circumzenithal arc is a flat arc of a large horizontal circle near the horizon. The upper arc occurs only when the angular altitude of the luminary is less than 32°; the lower arc occurs only when the angular altitude of the luminary is more than 58°. The upper arc touches the large halo, if visible, when the angular altitude of the luminary is about 22°; the lower arc touches the large halo when the angular altitude of the luminary is about 68°. The arcs become increasingly separated from the large halo as the angular altitude of the luminary departs from the above values. Circumzenithal arcs may be observed without the large halo being visible.

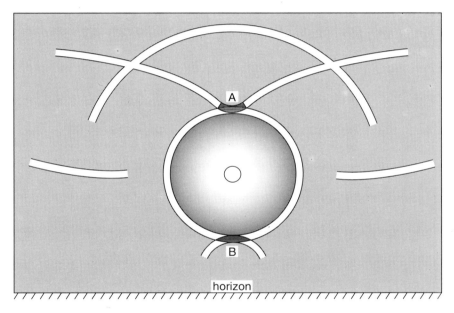

Figure 28.   Solar halo complex.

Witnessed from m.v. *Nova Scotia*, Captain N.R. Land, St John (N.B.) to Liverpool. Observer, Mr A.C. Herdan, 3rd Officer.

'1 October 1965. Position 43°16′ N, 66°15′W. The halo complex was clearly seen from 1200–1600 GMT. The radius of the inner halo was 21°26′ and that of the partial outer concentric halo was 46°30′. Two wing-shaped arcs, each subtending an angle of about 54′, crossed the outer concentric halo, meeting at the centre of their span directly above the sun and in contact with the upper edge of the inner concentric halo. At the point of contact (A) a brilliant spectrum could be seen subtending an angle of at least 1¼°. About 1530, the most vivid period, two more haloes were seen. One was a white arc which would have stretched right across the halo complex, passing through the position of the sun, if it had not been rendered invisible by the glare. The other was a small, but vivid, inverted half halo of about 6° radius; it was in contact with the inner halo, its upper edge crossing the latter's lower limb (B). At this point also vivid coloration was seen. Altitude of sun: 21°50′; bearing 094°. Cloud, small amounts of Cirrus and Altostratus.'

171

Two arcs of contact of this halo are known, the supralateral and infralateral tangential arcs of 46°. They are in contact, on the solar vertical, with the (upper) circumzenithal and the circumhorizontal arcs respectively. Also, they are bitangent or bitangential arcs in that, in the most general case, they contact the 46° halo (or at least, its theoretical position) at two points each and they are lateral tangential arcs in that these points of contact are not generally on the solar vertical. For the supralateral arc, when the solar elevation is less than 22°, the points of contact are on the upper sides of the halo, and they move towards its top as that elevation increases. At that critical solar elevation, the two contacts merge at the top of the halo, and for higher solar elevations up to 32° (when it ceases to be formed) the arc stands clear of the halo. At least in their upper parts, this arc and its parent halo are so similar in shape and so close together as to be liable to the confusion noted above.

For solar elevations less than 58°, the infralateral arc consists of two separate arcs concave to the sun and touching the 46° halo on its lower sides, nearer the bottom of the halo the higher the sun. At this critical solar elevation the lower ends of these two arcs merge on the solar vertical. At a solar elevation of 68° the two points of contact merge on the solar vertical, and for higher sun the single arc is detached from the position of the halo of 46°.

The observation and recording of haloes
High latitudes, especially the polar regions, are the most favourable for frequent and brilliant displays of halo phenomena, which can be formed not only by cirrostratus cloud, but also by ice fog. Many fine displays occur, however, in temperate latitudes, where the late spring is an especially good season.

Cirrostratus is the most favourable cloud for the production of halo phenomena; the thinner and more uniform its texture the better. On the most suitable occasions, the blue sky is only dimmed with a uniform milky appearance. When the cloud is thicker in some places than others, and especially when wisps and streaks of cirrus are mixed with it, not only are the phenomena less distinct but straight or curved lines of cloud may be mistaken for additional halo phenomena.

When thin cirrostratus is present and one or more of the commoner halo phenomena are well seen, the prospects of seeing some of the rare halo phenomena are good and a careful general look over the whole sky may result in something else being seen. Attention should chiefly be concentrated on the following regions (a) that surrounding the sun up to a radius of at least 46°, (b) a belt of the sky, at the same altitude as the sun, all round the horizon, (c) the overhead sky, with the zenith as centre.

A halo phenomenon is thus identified by its position in the sky; its appearance is of secondary importance, though, in some cases, this helps in the identification. The most essential part of a halo observation is therefore the determination of its position by angular measurement with reference to the sun (or moon) or, in appropriate cases, the horizon or the zenith. Most of the rarer phenomena can only thus be identified with certainty.

The altitude of the sun, to the nearest degree, should also always be given, since this affects the precise position of certain halo phenomena, and in some cases determines what phenomena it is possible to see at the time. The radius of the relatively well-defined inner edge of any halo, or part of a halo, centred on the sun should be measured in degrees from the sun's centre. Record what is measured as the radius of any halo, whether to an inner or outer edge or a brightest point. The sharpness of the edges may also be worth noting. In the case of arcs situated vertically above the sun such as the circumzenithal arc, the distance of the lowest part of the arc from the sun is all that is required. It is useful, however, to estimate the extent of any such arc as a fraction of the small circle of which it forms part.

The mock-sun ring
This is identified by its parallelism to the horizon, at the sun's altitude. It is probably worthwhile to check the elevation of this circle at one or two points other than the sun, as it has on rare occasions been seen tilted, and such checks on suspected fragments of the circle will render their identification more certain. A phenomenon situated on it, such as the anthelion or other bright spot, or the point of intersection of an arc with it, is measured in the form of azimuth distance from the sun. Even for the parhelia of 22°, checks on the theory are desirable, and this measurement will confirm the identity of any suspected anthelion. Most importantly, it will give insight into the precise mode of formation of any paranthelia seen.

The above statement should be sufficient to indicate to the observer the lines on which he should proceed. The most difficult cases are certain abnormal phenomena such as are shown in Figures 28 and 29. The diameter of any halo not centred on the sun or moon could be measured by sextant; the altitude and azimuth of the

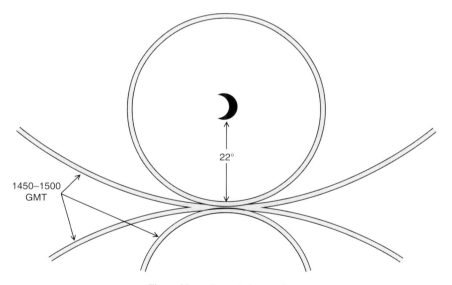

Figure 29.   Lunar halo complex.

Witnessed from m.v. *Koraki*. Captain H.C. Townend. Tauranga to Melbourne. Observer, Mr M.J.C. Orr, 2nd Officer.
'28 May 1967. Position 34°34'S, 171°42'E. The 22° halo was first seen at 1415 GMT when the moon was at an approximate altitude of 60° and bore 090°. At 1450 the tangential arcs appeared, weak at first but gradually gaining in intensity in the next 10 minutes. The complex remained visible for about 20 minutes, after which time only the 22° halo was seen. A thin layer of Cirrostratus to Altostratus was present and also some Cumulus.'

173

estimated centre of the halo would then give its position. The position of any detached arc could be measured by taking the altitude and azimuth of each of the two ends, and of the point on the halo equidistant from these.

Having established the position, any point of special interest should be noted, such as an exceptional degree of brightness or colour, variations in brightness in different parts of a halo, or a halo appearing elliptical instead of circular, etc. In the case of the rarer phenomena, the fullest possible information should be recorded, preferably accompanied by a sketch, on which all angular measurements are shown. In sketching halo phenomena the size of the sun (or moon) is usually exaggerated, sometimes very greatly. Even in landscape paintings by well-known artists, the same thing usually occurs. The discs of the sun and moon are about half a degree in diameter and therefore only about one-ninetieth of the diameter of the common halo of 22° radius.

Other halo phenomena

There are a few other phenomena not included in the previous pages, e.g. various forms of cross, centred on the sun or moon, are occasionally seen (Figure 30). The vertical arm is usually formed by part of a sun pillar and the horizontal arm by a short portion of the mock-sun circle. Haloes of other radii are occasionally seen (often several of them simultaneously), and so are rarer arcs, but the 'halo of 90°' sometimes referred to is probably a false association of reports of a number of distinct phenomena. One such observation is shown in Figure 28 in which is seen the ordinary 22° halo, with an arc above, possibly part of the 46° halo, but more likely its supralateral tangent arc.

The ideal method of recording halo phenomena is by colour photography, since, if the characteristics of the camera and its lens are known, the material is available for later analysis. An all-sky camera, if available, is particularly valuable.

Ideally, observed halo phenomena should be represented on the surface of a sphere or hemisphere or part thereof, but this is hardly ever practical: a flat sheet of

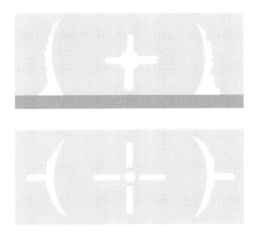

Figure 30.   Forms of halo cross.

174

paper is all that is available. In the representation on such of halo phenomena confined to a small area of sky, it is natural to represent any great-circle arc (or near-great small-circle arc) as a straight line, and any parallel arc as a parallel line. Unfortunately, the only real meaning of 'parallelism' in terms of the celestial-sphere geometry of halo phenomena is 'concentricity' (that is, only a small circle can be 'parallel' to any great circle) and this can lead to problems of representation.

For instance, if, with fairly low sun, the horizon be represented by a straight line, it is natural to represent the parhelia at the same distance from it as the sun is shown. But at higher sun, this obviously fails to represent adequately the fact that the parhelic **circle**, on whose position these phenomena are located, **is** a circle, centred on the zenith. If in any doubt, the best convention is to select a point to represent the zenith, describe as much of the horizon as is required as a circular arc centred on that point, and similarly centre circles or circular arcs indicating the positions of the parhelic circle and circumzenithal or circumhorizontal arcs on that point. It is unlikely that similarly drawing every halo observed to be circular (even great-circular) as a circle centred on the point selected to represent its centre will give rise to difficulty if the radii are carefully drawn, albeit that only a very artificial projection will have these characteristics. This has been done in Figs 27 and 28 to represent the arcs associated with the halo of 46°.

IRIDESCENT CLOUD

Patches of delicate, but often vivid, colouring are occasionally seen at any time of the day on altocumulus and other middle and high clouds, often covering quite a large extent of cloud. It may form a very beautiful spectacle, especially if the sun is hidden from the observer's view by lower cloud. Red and green are the most common colours, but others, such as lilac, may be seen. Sometimes the colours lie in bands parallel to the edge of the cloud, but often they form an irregular mosaic, delicately shading into one another. The colouring resembles that of coronae, but the bands of colour do not form concentric circles with the sun as centre. Sometimes a number of coloured patches may be seen along a straight line passing through the sun.

Iridescence is usually seen on cloud near the sun or within about 30° of the sun, but may occur at greater distances. It seems to be most frequently observed on cloud that is in the process of either formation or evaporation. The colouring is not normally seen after sunset or before sunrise, but brilliant iridescence, continuing after sunset, or appearing before sunrise, may be seen on a very rare high form of cloud, called 'mother-of-pearl cloud'.

If the observer is in doubt as to whether he is seeing ordinary sunset cloud colouring, or iridescent colouring towards the time of sunset, it should be remembered that the former may cover large areas of cloud, or many isolated clouds, with no colour. Iridescence, on the other hand usually shows much smaller areas of different colour on one cloud and the coloration is purer and more prismatic, in this respect resembling the colours of the rainbow.

When seen, remarks on the nature and extent of the colouring, the type of cloud and the approximate angular distance from the sun will be useful.

LIGHTNING

Anything unusual observed during a thunderstorm is worth recording. Some points in connection with lightning are given below.

Lightning varies in colour on different occasions: it is normally white, with perhaps a bluish tinge. Sometimes it is quite a bright violet. Other colours seen are reddish-white, yellowish-white, mauve and blue.

Variations of the ordinary appearance of forked lightning have been seen:

(a) Inequalities of brightness in different parts of the path, known as chain or beaded lightning, from the impression left on the eye.

(b) Rocket lightning, so called from the relative slowness of the flash, allowing the progressive lengthening of the streak to be seen.

A high frequency of visible flashes sometimes results from more than one storm in different directions being operative at the same time, so that at night there is almost continuous illumination of the sea or landscape. Such a lightning rate has been known to persist for several hours, but this is very unusual.

Occasional reports of ships being struck by lightning are received, but this event is probably of much less frequent occurrence than in the days of wooden sailing ships. Descriptions of the effect on the ship and on the compasses (see page 151) will be of interest. Observations of recent years show that in nearly all cases the foremast or fore part of the vessel is struck.

Ball lightning

The special form known as ball lightning resembles a ball of fire, either falling from a cloud or moving more or less horizontally. It usually lasts only a few seconds and may disappear noiselessly or with an abrupt clap of thunder. Ball lightning has been seen at close range and it has sometimes passed into or through a building. Rare forms of lightning have also been seen shooting upwards from the top of cumulonimbus cloud, in various branching or rocket-like forms.

Observations of ball lightning. Careful observations of this uncommon, but not extremely rare, form are specially desired. Observers should log the following points when ball lightning is seen:

1. Distance from observer.
2. Diameter, shape, colour and movement of ball.
3. Whether it is opaque or translucent.
4. Brightness, e.g. whether it is too bright to look at directly.
5. Whether or not it is rotating.
6. Whether the edge is sharp or fuzzy.
7. Any smell or sound associated with the ball.
8. Formation and disappearance.

Observations of ball lightning forming are particularly rare. A labelled drawing is always helpful. There are almost no acceptable photographs of ball lightning. Reports of damage done by ball lightning are useful, but care must be taken to distinguish this from damage done by an ordinary lightning strike.

Solar rainbow

The normal appearance of a bright rainbow is as follows. The chief or primary bow shows the sequence of colours, violet, indigo, blue, green, yellow, orange and red, the red being on the outside or top of the bow. In contact with the inside of this bow, one or two fainter 'supernumerary bows' can frequently be seen with the colours in the same order, the first inner bow being much fainter than the primary bow and the second fainter still. Supernumerary bows do not, however, show the full range of spectrum colours; they are essentially red, or red and green, though other colours may be seen. In cases of exceptionally brilliant rainbows up to five supernumerary bows may be seen.

Secondary rainbow. Concentric with the primary bow, but 9° outside it, is the secondary rainbow, in which the full range of colours appear in the reverse order, red inside and violet at the top or outside. The primary bow is formed by means of one internal reflection in each raindrop; the secondary bow is fainter, being produced by two such reflections. The sky between the primary and secondary bow is rather darker than that inside the primary bow, or the general sky in the neighbourhood. The secondary bow is commonly seen, but if the primary bow is faint the secondary one may not be visible.

Both the primary and secondary bows are seen when the observer has his back towards the sun. The sun, the observer's eye and the centres of the circles of which the primary and secondary rainbows form arcs, are always in a straight line, so that the azimuth of the highest part of the bow is 180° from the sun's azimuth. The normal radius of the arc of red light of the primary rainbow is 42°, of the violet arc 40¼°; in the secondary bow the radii are 51° for red light and 54° for violet light, all the values given being approximate. Hence the normal breadth of the primary bow is about 1¾° and that of the secondary bow about 3°. It also follows that with the sun at an altitude of 42° the uppermost point of the primary bow is on the horizon, its centre being 42° below the horizon, and hence no primary bow can be formed if the sun's altitude exceeds 42°. Similarly no secondary rainbow can be formed if the sun's altitude exceeds 54°. Consequently rainbows are mainly morning and evening phenomena; nearer midday, if seen at all, the arc of the bow is shorter and the altitude small. Thunderstorm rain passing away from the observer gives the most favourable circumstances for the production of bright rainbows.

When the observer is at ground level and the rain cloud is distant, the rainbow arcs are always less than semicircles, unless the sun is on the horizon, when they form semicircles. When, however, the rain is near, and especially if the observer is in an elevated position, such as on the bridge of a ship, the bows will be greater than a semicircle and may even form complete circles. Several accounts have been received of bows forming complete circles as far as the waterline on each side of the ship.

One of the halo phenomena, the circumzenithal arc, may show bright rainbow colouring, but is always in such a position that the observer must face the sun to see it.

Rainbow colouring. Rainbows do not always show the same colouring. The colours seen, and their relative width and intensity, vary according to the size of the raindrops producing the bow. The colours are most brilliant and best defined with very large raindrops such as occur in thunderstorm rain. With fairly large drops, vivid violet and green may be seen, and also pure red, but little or no blue. With smaller drops the red weakens and with still smaller ones the green goes, leaving only the violet. Just before sunset, when the sun is red in colour, especially in autumn and winter, an all-red rainbow may be produced.

White rainbow. If the raindrops are extremely small, as in the case in some cloud and in fog, a white rainbow may be formed. Such a bow is called a 'fog-bow' or 'Ulloa's Ring'. In all rainbows there is some overlapping of the colours; in a white rainbow the overlapping is so complete that white light is reconstituted. For a white rainbow to be seen, the observer must be near the cloud or near or in the fog.

Lunar rainbows

Lunar rainbows are formed in the same way as solar ones, but are considerably rarer, having regard to the comparatively short periods that a bright moon is above the horizon. A lunar rainbow is usually fainter than a solar one and it is not always possible to distinguish colour; the appearance is then whitish. Quite frequently, however, colour may be observed; more rarely the whole sequence of colour can be seen. Secondary and supernumerary lunar rainbows are very rarely seen, on account of their faintness.

Reflection rainbows

These are seen occasionally on calm days when a sheet of water lies in front of or behind the observer standing with his back to the sun. Such bows are formed by rays of light illuminating the falling raindrops after reflection at the surface of the sheet of water. The centre of a reflection rainbow is thus as high above the horizon as the sun, or the same angular distance above, as the centre of the direct bow is below the horizon; consequently the arc, when complete, exceeds a semicircle. The direct and reflection rainbows intersect on the horizon, and the colours have the same sequence.

Observation of rainbows

The observer who wishes to make useful observations of normal rainbows should record the colours seen, in sequence, with an indication of their relative widths and intensities. If supernumerary bows are seen below the primary bow, the number of these and their colouring should be noted. If the secondary bow is unusually bright it is worthwhile looking for supernumerary bows just above it; these have rarely been seen on account of their faintness. An additional primary bow may be seen when the sea is sufficiently calm to give a reflected image of the sun in the sea, which acts as the light source for the bow. The position of this bow with regard to that formed by the sun itself varies with the sun's altitude. The secondary bow from the sun's reflected image is almost always too faint to be observable.

Abnormal bows, or arcs of bows, perhaps intersecting the normal bows, and sometimes white in colour, have occasionally been seen and it is of special interest to record these as fully as possible, since no explanation has yet been found for some of them. They sometimes meet the horizon at the same point as one of the normal bows. In such cases the sequence of colour, or the absence of colour should be noted. It is essential to give angular measurements of such bows, in the form of azimuths of the ends of the bow or arc, in which case the sun's azimuth should also be given. If a normal bow is also seen, the difference in azimuth between the points where the normal and abnormal bows meet the horizon will serve to establish the position of the latter. If an abnormal bow is seen concentric with the normal primary or secondary bow the difference of altitude of the bows at their highest point should be given.

SCINTILLATION

Scintillation, or twinkling, is the more or less rapid change of apparent brightness of a star, accompanied also at relatively low altitudes by colour changes. It is due to minor changes in the refractive power of the atmosphere. The amount of twinkling is always greatest towards the horizon and least in the zenith. The general amount varies considerably on different nights, so that at the zenith twinkling may be considerable, slight or entirely absent. Nights without appreciable twinkling towards the horizon are rare. When the changes of brightness are small the fluctuations are slower; in proportion as they are greater they become more rapid.

Colour change is usually shown by stars at altitudes not exceeding 34°; it never occurs at altitudes greater than 51°. The brightest stars, e.g. Sirius, at low altitudes show it most and, in favourable conditions, the changes may be very striking, the star flashing blood-red, emerald-green, bright blue, etc.

Scintillation is also observed in the case of terrestrial lights. The shimmering seen near the ground on a hot day is akin to it.

The bright planets do not usually appear to twinkle, as they have discs of definite size, although these are not visible without optical aid. Each point on the disc twinkles independently of the others, so that on the average the light is steady. The planet Mercury, only seen in twilight and at relatively low altitudes may, however, be seen to twinkle because of the small size of its disc, and, exceptionally, other planets at very low altitudes may exhibit some twinkling.

The relative degree of twinkling in different parts of the world, e.g. in temperate as compared with tropical latitudes, is not very well known and any information bearing on this will be of interest. It is probably greatest in temperate latitudes, which are subject to the passage of depressions.

SKY COLORATION, DAYTIME

The light of the sky in daytime is due to the illumination of the atmosphere by sunlight. The molecules of air exert a selective action on the colour constituents of sunlight, scattering mainly blue rays in all directions and letting the others pass on.

Dust is always present in greater or less degree in the atmosphere, and in certain states of weather larger particles are present in the lower part of the atmosphere. The presence of dust tends to weaken the blue of the sky, because each particle reflects the whole of the white light. The greater the number of particles and the larger their size the more the sky becomes whitish-blue. For the same reason the cloudless sky is always whiter near the horizon than at higher altitudes. After heavy rain, such as that due to the passage of a depression, the larger dust particles have been washed out of the air and the sky is often a very deep blue.

The sky is often whitened within the region of smoke pollution from a large town. Natural dust from desert sources, at higher levels in the air, also has the same effect, e.g. the white skies seen in the region of the East Indies in the south-east monsoon, caused by dust from the Australian desert. The dust from great volcanic eruptions may whiten the sky for weeks or months afterwards, over more or less considerable areas of the globe. After the Krakatoa eruption the colour of the sky at various times of the day in equatorial regions was described as white, smoky, yellowish or reddish.

The unclouded sky may also be whitened by what is known as 'optical haze', which also makes distant terrestrial objects indistinct. This occurs on hot days and is the result of innumerable little convective uprisings of air, causing confused and variable refraction of light. The shimmering of terrestrial objects on a hot day also results from the same cause.

The sky may sometimes be covered by a layer of cirrostratus, so thin and uniform as not to be visible as cloud, but sufficient to dim the blueness, giving the sky a milky appearance.

A somewhat dirty green coloration of clear patches in a generally overcast sky is sometimes seen at sea in the daytime, not to be confused with the green coloration of part of the clear twilight sky in the west. This day-time coloration is associated with bad or windy weather, or is considered a prognostic of such weather. Observations of it and of the accompanying or subsequent weather will be welcomed, as it is not yet fully understood. It appears to occur most frequently in the Roaring Forties.

SKY COLORATION AT TWILIGHT

When clouds, particularly middle and upper clouds, occur about the time of sunset or sunrise, or in bright twilight, their coloration is often very beautiful. The cloud colours are mainly shades of orange, rose or red, since the direct sunlight illuminating the cloud has passed through a great length of the lower layers of the atmosphere. Shades of purple are sometimes seen, since a cloud may at the same time be indirectly illuminated by scattered blue light from higher atmospheric levels. On rare occasions colouring of exceptional magnificence occurs.

Colour phenomena also occur in a cloudless sky during the twilight periods. These vary considerably and are best developed in arid or semi-arid land regions. Some of those which occur more commonly everywhere are mentioned here. The Primary Twilight Arch appears after the sun has set, as a bright, but not very sharply defined segment of reddish, or yellowish light, resting on the western horizon. After the sun has set, a pink or purple glow may be seen, covering a considerable part of the western sky, known as the First Purple Light. It reaches its greatest brightness when the sun is about 4° below the horizon, and disappears when it is about 6° below.

At sunset, a steely-blue segment, darker than the rest of the sky, begins to rise from the eastern horizon. This is the shadow of the earth thrown by the sun on to the Earth's atmosphere. The Earth-shadow is bordered by a narrow band of rose or purple colour, called the Counterglow. The whole rises fairly quickly in altitude, the shadow encroaching on the counterglow and soon obliterating it. With increasing general darkness the edge of the shadow weakens, but may sometimes be traced up to its passage through the zenith. In the later stages of twilight, this shadow edge has come down nearly to the western horizon, leaving a slightly more luminous segment between it and the horizon. This is the Secondary Twilight Arch. Just before the ending of astronomical twilight, it is sometimes seen as a fairly well defined whitish arch on the horizon, with an altitude of only a few degrees at its apex. This might be confused with an auroral arc visible at very low altitude.

Analogous phenomena, in the reverse order, occur before sunrise. Other colours are often seen in the cloudless twilight sky, portions of which may be green, yellow, orange or red, according to the amount of dust and water vapour present in the air. Instead of the purple light after sunset, the sky very often shows some shade of clear green, probably when the air is relatively free from dust.

SKY COLORATION AT NIGHT

Between the visible stars, brighter and fainter, the background of the clear night sky is not wholly dark. Part of the general luminosity of the sky is due to the accumulated light of the brighter telescopic stars, which cannot be seen as individual stars with the unaided eye. The remainder is due to the airglow, which may vary in intensity on different nights, see page 151. The airglow is greenish in colour but it is usually too faint for the colour to be seen. In bright moonlight the sky is generally somewhat greenish, but it is probable that when the air is relatively dust-free and the full moon is at high altitude it becomes bluish. Opinion varies on this point, as the colour of faint light is not equally well seen by different persons.

TWILIGHT

Twilight is due to the illumination of the higher levels of the atmosphere by the sun when this is below the observer's horizon. The last stage of twilight is very faint and indefinite and it is not possible to say exactly when it ends. Astronomical twilight is defined as ending in the evening when the sun's centre is 18° below the horizon, since by that time sixth magnitude stars, the faintest that can be seen by the naked eye, have become visible in the region of the zenith.

Another and shorter twilight period, that of civil twilight, is recognized; this ends in the evening when the sun is 6° below the horizon. This is assumed to mark the ending of the time when outdoor labour is possible. The period of civil twilight is important to the seaman because experience has shown that subsequent to it the horizon is not sufficiently clearly visible to obtain good stellar observations. In the later stages of civil twilight such observations can be made, the brighter fixed stars being visible and the horizon still remaining clearly visible. Similar definitions apply to morning twilight.

The duration of twilight varies according to the latitude. It is shortest in the tropics where the apparent track of the sun down to the horizon is steepest. It also varies to some extent at different seasons, being shortest in all latitudes about the time of the equinoxes.

The following tables show the extent of these variations between the equator and latitude 60° N or S; AT and CT refer to astronomical and civil twilight respectively.

	Equator		30°		50°		60°	
	AT	CT	AT	CT	AT	CT	AT	CT
	h min	h min	h min	h min	h min	h min	h min	h min
Midwinter ...	1 16	0 26	1 26	0 31	2 1	0 45	2 48	1 9
Equinoxes ...	1 10	0 24	1 20	0 28	1 52	0 37	2 31	0 48
Midsummer ...	1 15	0 26	1 37	0 32	—	0 51	—	1 59

In the belt between latitude 48½° N and the Arctic Circle there is no true night for some weeks of the midsummer period, as the sun does not sink as much as 18° below the horizon. There is a similar belt in the southern hemisphere, six months later, during the southern summer. In polar regions there is a long twilight period of about two months between the long polar periods of summer daylight and winter night.

At rare intervals abnormally long duration of twilight is observed. This is caused by the presence of fine dust suspended in the upper air. The dust may be due to a great volcanic eruption, such as that of Krakatoa in 1883 or to the fall of an exceptionally large meteor, such as that of 30 June 1908 in Siberia. Observations of exceptionally bright and long-continued twilight will be of value.

WATERSPOUTS

A waterspout is a whirlwind over the sea, appearing as a funnel-shaped column usually extending from the lower surface of cumulonimbus cloud to the sea. In travelling over the sea this column often becomes oblique or bent; it may become looped. The spout is in rapid rotation and the wind around it follows a circular path. Although very local, this wind is often violent, causing confused but not high sea. A noise of 'rushing wind' may be heard. In most cases, a waterspout forms downwards from the base of the cloud, appearing in its early stages as a dark funnel hanging from the cloud. The sea surface below becomes agitated and the funnel finally dips into the centre of the spray. The waterspout may last from a few minutes up to half an hour or more. Sometimes the spout, formed of condensed water vapour, does not reach the sea, and retreats up into the cloud. Several may be seen at the same time.

Formation. There are a number of theories which attempt to explain the formation of a waterspout. These theories may be classified into those which relate to the origin of the more severe tornado storm spout of the tropics and subtropics, and those which relate to the milder 'fair weather' spout of tropical and temperate latitudes.

The tornado spout. This may form over the sea but is more likely to have formed over land and subsequently to have passed out to sea. Its formation may result from the horizontal shear between warm and cold air currents existing up to considerable heights in the atmosphere. Such conditions normally occur along a cold front or cold occlusion surface. The tornado storm waterspout may damage even a large vessel if it passes directly over it, the damage being caused partly by tornadic winds, partly by the deluge of water sometimes released, and partly by the suddenly reduced pressure, although this effect has probably been exaggerated.

The 'fair weather' waterspout. This type of waterspout is believed to be formed partly by convection processes. Under conditions of a high temperature lapse rate near the sea surface, a small parcel of warm air becomes a little warmer than its environment and begins to rise. Rotation is caused by the converging surface winds sucked in under the rising air parcel and energy gained by the atmospheric instability is augmented by the latent heat of condensation of the water vapour present. The initial convectional ascending air current may occur directly below cumulonimbus cloud in which case it may penetrate the cloud, and the rotation increases until a complete waterspout is formed. Although the 'fair weather' waterspout should cause no real damage to a larger vessel, it should be avoided by the small-boat mariner.

Frequency of waterspouts

Though waterspouts are infrequent in high latitudes, their frequency does not depend wholly on latitude: indeed, a number have been reported from North Sea oil platforms. In general, more are observed in lower latitudes but their frequency in tropical and equatorial regions varies considerably in different oceans. Waterspouts are commonest in the following regions: Equatorial Atlantic, South Atlantic, eastern coast of the United States south of 35° N, Gulf of Mexico, eastern Mediterranean, Bay of Bengal and the Gulf of Thailand.

Observations of waterspouts

Sketches or photographs of waterspouts, and details of the mode of formation and dissipation, are of value. The diameter of the spout and the direction of rotation should be noted. If it is possible to determine the rate of rotation, this information is very valuable. Sometimes a streak or mark on the spout enables this to be done. The spout is a hollow tube; double-walled spouts have occasionally been recorded. The approximate vertical height of a spout may be found by vertical sextant angle, together with the estimated distance from ship. The height of a waterspout from sea surface to cloud base is usually from 1000 ft (300 m) to 2000 ft (600 m). It may, however, be as little as 100 ft (30 m) or as much as 5000 ft (1500 m). There is a marked variation in observed diameters of waterspouts, from about 1 m up to about 200 m. The weather conditions, including instrumental readings, should be logged before, during and after the sighting of a waterspout; it is also helpful to know the position of the spout relative to the parent cloud and relative to any shower falling from it, e.g. whether the spout was at the leading edge or the rear of the cloud.

CHAPTER 12

MARINE PHENOMENA

OBSERVATIONS OF MARINE LIFE

For well over a hundred years the weather observing logs submitted by British mariners to the Met. Office have been accompanied by recordings of marine life. The extent of these thousands of biological reports over time and space makes them of special importance. Seamen will know that their observations are highly valued by those scientists who receive them, and that reports from merchant ships may sometimes be the first and only indication of an event of ocean-wide significance.

Biological sightings may be grouped as follows:

(a)   Mammals, mostly whales.
(b)   Birds.
(c)   Fish.
(d)   Invertebrates.
(e)   Mass plankton effects such as bioluminescence, red tides and discoloured water.

A few reptiles such as turtles and sea snakes may be reported. Insects, commonly noted, always originate from land, often as stowaways; there is only one truly marine insect, a relative of the pond skaters, and even this lives on the surface of the water, not in it.

It may be instructive to list the groups most frequently reported in recent years. The most commonly reported cetaceans are sperm whales, followed by pilot whales, beaked whales generally, humpback whales, bottle-nosed dolphins, killer whales, blue whales and minke whales. In the case of fish, hammerhead sharks are the commonest, followed by manta rays, flying fish, white-tipped sharks, hatchet fish and sunfish; among invertebrates the By-the-Wind Sailor (*Velella*) and Portuguese Man-o'-War (*Physalia*) occur most of all, followed by swimming crabs and squid.

Everyone is aware that some watchkeepers keep a better lookout than others. Some have better eyesight, some have a naturally high level of attentiveness and some are less easily bored by watching the sea and sky separated by the straight line of the horizon. Nevertheless, the sharp-eyed spotting of sea-surface life is only the beginning of a useful observation. Those who first sight a marine organism may not necessarily make the best report.

Intellectual curiosity is needed and can be increased by reading. It is suggested that anyone interested in sea life should possess a few books of identification. There are many good books for home waters and several for global groups such as whales and seabirds, while for other waters it is best to search in local bookshops in ports visited for anglers' guides and other publications on marine life. These will be found more useful than the thickest tome for the wrong ocean. Back numbers of *The Marine Observer* contain many good descriptions and sketches of creatures actually seen by seamen from the deck of a ship, and may prove instructive.

Observers should try and draw what they have seen. An outline drawing, however simple, is one of the best aids to identification. As the drawing is made, careful observation of a whale or fish may reveal how many fins there are and how they are disposed. If the fish is not caught it should be drawn at once, before the memory fades. If the subject is an invertebrate, it should be drawn live in a bucket of water if possible, and notes added as to its size, colour and behaviour. Photographs are always useful but cannot be relied upon to show up the important features which can be highlighted by a line drawing. A photograph and drawing together is the best combination.

The importance of recording the occurrence of common animals as well as the unusual ones needs to be emphasized. Sightings of *Velella* or a hammerhead are as treasured as those of rare beasts: it is the common animals that are important, simply by being common. From many observations we can map their distribution and density, and perhaps learn how this distribution may change over the years.

ABNORMAL COMPASS DEVIATIONS

A ship's magnetic compass may show appreciable deviation during the progress of a considerable or severe magnetic storm (see Magnetic Disturbances, page 151).

When an aurora of an active type is seen especially in latitudes lower than those in which aurora is normally seen, the possibility of deflections of the magnetic compass should always be borne in mind. Mere brightness of aurora in a region where aurora frequently occurs is no criterion of the occurrence of a magnetic storm, e.g. a bright, colourless and relatively quiescent aurora seen in August or September in the western Atlantic on the Belle Isle route.

If a ship happens to be struck by lightning, a sudden abnormal deviation of the compass may result. This error may be of a temporary or a permanent nature. Chronometers and other equipment may also be affected.

Abnormal magnetic variation occurs locally in various regions. These variations, if experienced, should always be recorded, particularly if no mention of abnormal variation is made in the appropriate Admiralty Sailing Directions or on Admiralty charts of the region.

ABNORMAL RISES OF SEA LEVEL AND ABNORMAL WAVES

Both these phenomena are popularly included in the term 'tidal waves', but neither has any connection with the tides. If either occurs, however, at a coast in conjunction with a high tide, its effect will obviously be greater and more destructive.

Abnormal rises of sea level, on which ordinary sea and swell waves are superimposed, are produced by severe storms. High water levels are thus caused on many coasts, but fortunately the rise is rarely large enough to cause great damage. With strong westerly winds the water level at Cuxhaven, at the mouth of the Elbe, may rise 2½ metres above the normal. On exceptional occasions the rise has reached 3½ metres above the normal. Destructive rises mainly occur in connection with tropical storms; rises of as much as 6 and 4½ metres have been experienced on different sections of the east coast of the United States.

Submarine earthquakes and landslides, and violent volcanic eruptions near a coast or on an island, produce abnormal waves. Sometimes these are visible waves, at other times shock waves, the latter giving the sensation in severe cases of the ship having struck a rock. The visible waves may travel many hundreds of miles, or in very severe disturbances many thousands of miles.

Single high waves in fair weather, with smooth or moderate sea, are almost certainly of seismic origin. Sometimes there may be two or more such waves at intervals. On the other hand, isolated giant waves which have been reported in gale conditions, are probably caused by a synchronism of the larger waves in a sea or swell cycle. Some of these have been estimated to reach or exceed a height of 24 metres.

Abnormal waves

There have been, in recent years, a number of reports of abnormal waves causing considerable damage to quite large ships. There have also been reports of smaller vessels lost without trace possibly as a result of the action of such waves. It has thus become recognized that from time to time, particularly in certain sea areas, there can occur very unusual or 'freak' waves, the causes of which are not yet fully understood and concerning whose frequency we do not know nearly enough.

Freak waves

A 'freak' wave has recently been defined as a wave of very considerable height ahead of which there is a deep trough, so that it is the steepness of the wave which is its outstanding feature and which makes it dangerous to shipping. Many of the reports of 'freak' waves have come from an area off the coast of south-east Africa during the period May to October. It is thought to be very significant that this is an area where a strong current (the Agulhas Current) runs counter to the high seas generated by the rather frequent south-westerly gales of the winter months and also to the unusually heavy swells which spread north-eastwards from the Southern Ocean at that time of the year.

Theory indicates that a counter current opposes the advance of the wave energy through a sea and that when the current speed reaches one-quarter of the speed of the waves the wave energy will be trapped, leading to an area of steep and confused waves beyond which there is a patch of relatively calm water. In practice this is not consistent with the very occasional occurrence of a very high wave, produced by sea and swell waves getting into phase, whose front is much steepened by an opposing current.

There are probably other ocean areas where conditions favourable for these 'freak' waves occur from time to time, e.g. in the vicinity of the Gulf Stream in a period of north-easterly gale. More information is greatly needed. Whenever these abnormal wave conditions are met with they should be reported in as much detail as possible. Besides the exact time and position, weather conditions and the course and speed of the ship, information is needed about wind and wave conditions, both before and after the encounter, about any other factors which may influence the state of the sea, and of course a full description of the 'freak' wave itself together with a brief note about any damage sustained. This information should be entered in the 'Freak Wave Report' or 'Additional Remarks' sections of the meteorological logbook.

Mariners have a unique opportunity to observe many species of birds, which most of us can only read about.

Seabirds. Some species such as shearwaters, albatrosses and petrels, are pelagic and roam the oceans of the world, where they are seen following in the ship's wake, or feeding in areas rich in plankton and other small invertebrates. But they come to land only on remote islands. Ashore, many are heard rather more often than seen, because they nest in deep burrows, and move only by night. Gulls, terns and skuas are mainly coastal, although many make long journeys on migration; the Arctic Tern makes a 25 000-mile annual journey from its breeding areas, often within the Arctic Circle, to winter in the Antarctic.

Landbirds. Vast numbers of landbirds also migrate across the sea, for example across the Bay of Biscay, eastern Atlantic and the Mediterranean from Europe to Africa and back. There are many similar areas of high density: the western Atlantic, Caribbean and Gulf of Mexico, the Gulf of Aden and Arabian Sea, and many areas in the Pacific. Most of these landbirds travel by night, at heights of about 5000 feet, unseen except on aero-radar. But when disoriented by fog or clouds obscuring the star patterns, or when tired by headwinds, they descend to rest aboard anything in sight. Ships can provide a haven of rest, and in adverse migration weather these 'falls' of birds can be spectacular, involving several hundreds of many species. Most often reported are the large, extrovert or multicoloured species such as ospreys and hoopoes, and many species of herons and egrets, kingfishers, and birds of prey such as falcons, hawks and owls. Some of these will hitchhike aboard ships for hundreds of miles, often in the 'wrong' direction, preying on the much more numerous and smaller warblers, finches, wagtails, robins, swallows and like species.

Royal Naval Birdwatching Society

Thus the identification of birds at sea can become an absorbing pastime as well as a fascinating hobby. The Royal Naval Birdwatching Society (RNBWS) was founded in 1946 to co-ordinate the activities of RN bird-watchers at sea, but has progressively widened its membership to include all who share a common interest in birds and the sea itself. Up to 100 Merchant Navy officers and ratings are members of the RNBWS, sending in contributions from many of the world's oceans, using specially designed reporting and census forms. Identification is greatly assisted by accurate descriptions, sketches and photographs, together with details of geographical positions, dates, wind and weather conditions. Such observations can have a unique scientific value, and analyses of these and extracts of meteorological logbooks from weather reporting ships, are published in the society's annual journal *Sea Swallow,* to provide a unique source of data, built up over 44 years. The UK Met. Office can put would-be members in touch with the RNBWS.

Seabirds under threat

Some seabird species are under threat of extinction because of the combined effect of damage to their breeding areas and feeding grounds. The culprit in both cases is often Man himself, either due to perdition by introduced cats and rats or by direct damage to the fragile ecology of the breeding islands; over fishing and pollution can upset the balance of food available in their feeding grounds. There is thus a growing worldwide interest in these phenomena and scientists need to know much more about their distribution, their feeding methods and their movements in the non-breeding season. Seafarers can therefore play an important role in establishing the facts.

DOLPHIN AND WHALE OBSERVATIONS

Identification of cetaceans (Latin: *cetus*, whale) at sea is not easy, as most of the animal cannot be seen and even when on occasion they leap clear of the surface it is only momentary. However, observing and recording sightings of cetacea can be a very rewarding experience.

Identification. The various cetacean species often appear very similar to one another and must be carefully examined before they can be identified with any degree of certainty. Every species has one or more characteristic similar to those of another and by systematically working through a set of characteristics there is a greater chance of identifying any particular species. The behaviour of any species often changes according to the circumstances and although helpful this behaviour may not always be as reliable as the morphological characteristics.

Whales
In the case of the large whales, the larger the whale, generally the smaller and further back is the dorsal fin. The ways in which the whale surfaces, blows and dives are, when added to size and colour characteristics, useful to know before attempting an identification. In the case of smaller whales and dolphins, especially where known distribution patterns overlap, identification becomes even more difficult because there are many more options to consider. In addition to making general descriptions, observers at sea can aid identification by experts, as well as adding to their knowledge of these intelligent creatures, by answering all or some of the following questions:

(a) *Large whales, over 9 metres in length*

1. What is the overall size of the whale?
2. Was it seen to blow, at what interval? Was the blow from the front of the head or from some way back? What was the height, shape and angle of the blow? Did it blow before the appearance of the dorsal fin?
3. What is the height, shape and position of the dorsal fin? (Note the angle the dorsal fin forms with the whale's back, e.g. more or less then 40°.)
4. During the roll-over between blows, how much of the back shows? Is it more or less than the height of the dorsal fin?
5. Can you see the forelimbs and are they long or short?
6. When the whale dives, how does it dive? Does it bunch up its hindquarters or seem to sink on a more or less even keel? Are the flukes raised above the surface on diving? Observing the flukes, what shape are they, do they have smooth or serrated edges and are they the same colour on both sides?

7. Can you see any throat grooves, crenellations, growths or ridges, etc. on the head or body of the whale?

8. Can you see any baleen in the mouth, and if so, what colour is it?

9. What is the whale's general shape and colour pattern?

(b) *Medium sized whales, 4.5 to 9 metres in length*

1. What is the overall size?

2. Can you see the shape of the head, and does it have a beak or noticeable forehead? Are any teeth or baleen visible?

3. Is the dorsal fin mid-point or aft, and what shape and height is it?

4. What is the whale's general shape and colour pattern? If there are any visible marks or scratches, are they single or double, such as 'tramlines'?

(c) *Small whales, including dolphins and porpoises*

1. What is the overall size?

2. What is the shape of the head and length of beak (if any)?

3. What is the size and shape of the dorsal fin?

4. Is the animal long and thin or generally robust?

5. Are there any clear bands or shapes in the colour pattern, and if there is any noticeable 'plimsoll line', how broad is it?

6. Make a sketch of the colour pattern and note whether the colours merge into one another or there are clear demarcations.

MARINE BIOLUMINESCENCE

Many marine organisms have the ability to produce light. This phenomenon is known as bioluminescence and it occurs in many different visible forms. Most bioluminescence observed from a ship at sea is induced by the turbulence of the wake or bow wave, and is usually made up of the responses of many different organisms. Nevertheless this visible bioluminescence is frequently dominated by the contribution of certain microscopic forms which are present in abundance in the surface waters.

Types of bioluminescence. Although the most frequently encountered phenomenon is a relatively uniform glow, interspersed with occasional flashes from larger animals, there are also a number of more remarkable manifestations reported by observers at sea. These include:

(a) A diffuse white luminescence which extends over a very large area and may even give enough light to read by. This is known as 'white water' or 'milky sea' and is encountered particularly often in the Arabian Sea area. It is believed to be caused by luminous bacteria at the surface.

(b) Rapid flashes of light in the sea.

(c) Upwelling of subsurface water or organisms breaking into vivid luminosity at the surface.

(d) Lines or parallel bands of bioluminescence which may be travelling through the water.

(e)   Great systems of bands rotating round a central hub like the spokes of a wheel. These often develop from moving parallel bands and are known as 'phosphorescent wheels'. More than one wheel may be visible at once, rotating in the same or opposite directions.

Most of our knowledge of the varied forms of bioluminescent phenomena has been derived from the observations recorded in ships' meteorological logbooks and these will continue to be of the greatest value. The accumulation of eyewitness reports, together with the research by marine biologists on particular species, will provide the means for better interpretation of the causes of the phenomena and their significance in the ecology of the oceans.

Recording observations of bioluminescence
Observations should always be as precise and as detailed as possible and should include quantitative estimations wherever practicable. Examples of these are the size of what appear to be individual organisms, or the direction, rate, length and width of luminous bands. A water sample is always very helpful if it can be treated with a convenient preservative. Ideally, the addition of formaldehyde to give a 5 per cent solution will leave the contents of the water easily identifiable. If formaldehyde is not available, alcohol can be used, even in the form of branded spirits, but the alcohol content of the diluted sample should be at least 10 per cent. Tincture of iodine can also be used to good effect. In any case a record of whether the water sample was luminous when shaken or stirred would be useful, and whether any organisms were visible in the sample.
   It is important to recognize that the degree to which the observer is dark adapted can make a great difference to his ability to see bioluminescence, and particularly to his estimate of its colour. The colour of a weak light is very difficult to assess unless the observer is adequately dark adapted because the colour sensitivity of the human eye changes with the light conditions. Whenever the bioluminescence is bright enough an estimate of its colour can be very useful in its interpretation.

Forms of bioluminescence
It is now possible to classify the various forms of bioluminescent phenomena and to interpret the causes of some of them with reasonable confidence. However, there are still many cases where we do not know either the organisms involved or the stimulus producing the light emission. For example, many of the apparent rates of movement of luminous patches, bands or wheels are too great to be caused by movements of the organisms themselves. A particularly puzzling phenomenon is the appearance of luminescence in the air a few feet above the surface of the sea when there is no obvious light in the water.

Phosphorescent wheels
Those fortunate enough to observe moving parallel bands or a phosphorescent wheel should in particular try to give an estimate of the time interval between successive bands or spokes and the direction of rotation. How far from the ship was it, and did the pattern change? It is often possible to conduct simple experiments which can add substantially to the value of the report:

1.　What is the result of flashing a light, such as an Aldis lamp, on the sea? Sometimes this will greatly increase the level of bioluminescence.

2.　Does turning the radar off have any effect? There are a few reports which suggest the radar may have had a stimulatory effect, but they need to be substantiated.

3.　Does stopping or changing the main engine r.p.m. have any effect? There are no reports of a phosphorescent wheel from sailing vessels, and it is therefore possible that they are induced by the engine vibrations of modern vessels. There are no known reports of the results of stopping engines whilst observing a wheel.

Voluntary observing ships and others may often be in the right place, and at the right time, to encounter bioluminescent phenomena that would otherwise go unnoticed. Logbook reports make these encounters available worldwide and provide the information that is essential to help us understand the oceans and their inhabitants more clearly.

SEA COLORATION

The normal colour of the sea in the open ocean in middle and low latitudes is an intense blue or ultramarine. The following modifications occur elsewhere:

(a)　In all coastal regions and in the open sea in higher latitudes, where the minute floating animal and vegetable life of the sea, called plankton, is in greater abundance, the blue of the sea is modified to shades of bluish-green and green. This results from a soluble yellow pigment, given off by the plant constituents of the plankton.

(b)　When the plankton is very dense, the colour of the organisms themselves may discolour the sea, giving it a more or less intense brown or red colour. The Red Sea, Gulf of California, the region of the Peru Current, South African waters and the Malabar Coast of India are particularly liable to this, seasonally.

(c)　The plankton is sometimes killed more or less suddenly, by changes of sea temperature etc., producing dirty-brown or grey-brown discoloration and 'stinking water'. This occurs on an unusually extensive scale at times off the Peruvian coast, where the phenomenon is called 'Aguaje'.

(d)　Larger masses of animate matter, such as fish spawn or floating kelp, may produce other kinds of temporary discoloration.

(e)　Mud brought down by rivers produces discoloration, which in the case of the great rivers may affect a large sea area. Soil or sand particles may be carried out to sea by wind or duststorms, and volcanic dust may fall over a sea area. In all such cases the water is more or less muddy in appearance. Submarine earthquakes may also produce mud or sand discoloration in relatively shallow water, and oil has sometimes been seen to gush up. The sea may be extensively covered with floating pumice stone after a volcanic eruption.

It is desirable to record all cases of unusual sea coloration. To determine the cause, microscopic examination of a sample may be necessary, and whenever possible a sample should be taken for subsequent examination at the Institute of Oceanographic Sciences Deacon Laboratory. The sample can be preserved for a considerable time if a few drops of 40 per cent formalin or of a strong solution of mercuric chloride are added.

CHAPTER 13

ORGANIZATION OF VOLUNTARY METEOROLOGICAL WORK AT SEA

Historical

Lieutenant Matthew Fontaine Maury of the US Navy was the first man to realize the scientific and commercial value of weather information collected from ships. Owing to his initiative, the first International Meteorological Conference was held at Brussels in 1853 to consider international co-operation and a uniform system of observation. As a result of this conference the British Met. Office was established as a department of the Board of Trade in 1854, with Captain (later Vice-Admiral) Robert FitzRoy as its head.

On assuming office, FitzRoy issued a circular letter to the masters of merchant ships, inviting their co-operation in observing the weather at sea, and by 1855, 105 ships of the Mercantile Marine and 32 ships of the Royal Navy were equipped with instruments for this purpose.

Observations were originally recorded in a 'Weather Register' whose general form was agreed at the Brussels conference. In 1874, Captain Henry Toynbee, who had then been Marine Superintendent of the Met. Office for seven years, drew up a 'Meteorological Log' based upon the original weather register but incorporating improvements. This was approved internationally and brought into use by the Met. Office for British ships. This log has been the means of providing climatological atlases for all oceans and has provided a basis for scientific investigation. The log underwent little change up to the end of World War I, when the use of climatological logbooks was gradually discontinued in favour of observations made at synoptic hours and transmitted by radio.

In 1953 and again in 1982 the method of setting out the observations was rearranged to produce the present-day meteorological logbook which is a combined record of observations made and radio weather messages sent. In the early 1980s the use of the Selected Ship log was extended to a number of offshore drilling rigs and platforms which act as observing units around the UK and the Continental Shelf. As a result of a monitoring exercise carried out between 1988 and 1990 with the co-operation of voluntary observers aboard ships of several countries, small changes were made in 1994 to the code groups recording wet-bulb and sea temperatures, to give a more accurate picture to the climatologists of the methods employed.

Weather registers and logs received from ships since the inception of the Met. Office in 1854, and some earlier isolated examples, as well as many other historical weather records such as Admiral Beaufort's original wind scale, are stored at the National Meteorological Archive in the Scott Building, Eastern Road, Bracknell, and can be seen by members of the public by arrangement.

The invention of wireless telegraphy opened up a new era in marine meteorology. As early as 1906, HM ships sent observations to the Met. Office by radio, while in

1909 a number of transatlantic liners commenced a similar service of reports by radio. Owing to the disruption caused by World War I, it was not until 1921, as a result of arrangements made by the International Meteorological Organization, that radio weather messages from merchant ships were organized on a satisfactory scale, and an international code was introduced for the purpose. In this year a number of Selected Ships commenced not only recording their observations, but transmitting them by radio in a special code at the internationally agreed hours of 00, 06, 12 and 1800 UTC. These messages were sent from all oceans through designated shore radio stations to various meteorological centres in accordance with an international scheme.

The number of ships which continued merely to record their observations six times daily, at the end of each watch, was gradually reduced as the number recording and reporting at the synoptic hour was increased. Today almost all observing ships report at the main synoptic hours, whilst some make additional three-hourly observations in the North Atlantic by special request. The data recorded in this manner can still be used for climatological purposes, in addition to their prime use in drawing up synoptic charts and hence in forecasting. The only exceptions are ships on short coastal passages, particularly ferries, whose time at sea is limited but whose observations at random times are nevertheless valuable.

At a meeting of the International Convention for Safety of Life at Sea (SOLAS), held in 1929, provision was made for the international encouragement of meteorological work at sea. The Convention was revised in 1948, in 1960 and again in 1974, with a Protocol added in 1978 and further amendments in later years.

During World War II observations from merchant ships again ceased. In 1946, as a result of a conference held in London, it was agreed that all meteorological services of the British Commonwealth would co-operate in organizing meteorological work at sea. In 1947 the International Meteorological Organization introduced a new universal code for the sending of radio weather messages by voluntary observing ships of all nations.

Throughout the history of the Marine Division of the Met. Office, observations have been made at sea on a voluntary basis. The number of ships making observations at any time depends upon requirements but is limited by practical considerations. The masters and officers of ships undertaking this work are referred to as the 'Corps of Voluntary Marine Observers', their ships comprising the 'Voluntary Observing Fleet'.

Marine Meteorology and the British Commonwealth. The arrangements for this generally follow those organized and kept up to date by the World Meteorological Organization (see page 195).

Voluntary Observing Ships of all nations are divided into three main classes: 'Selected Ships', 'Supplementary Ships' and 'Auxiliary Ships'. The first-named observe wind, weather, pressure and barometric tendency, temperatures, clouds and waves. They are equipped with a precision aneroid barometer, a barograph, wet- and dry-bulb thermometers in a modified marine screen, and sea thermometer and bucket.

Supplementary Ships make the same observations with the exception of barometric tendency, sea temperature and waves, and are not therefore equipped with barograph, bucket or sea thermometer.

Auxiliary Ships make similar observations to those made by Supplementary Ships, except that they do not report cloud. They use their own instruments, which have been previously checked by a Port Met. Officer to observe pressure and temperature. Their observations, recorded on a special form supplied for the purpose, are particularly useful when sailing in areas where shipping is normally sparse.

In addition to the above, many ships engaged in the coastwise and short-sea trades around the British Isles are supplied with a sea-temperature bucket and thermometers. They transmit sea-water temperatures to the UK Met. Office which are particularly useful in the forecasting of fog, and when in the North Sea they include reports of wind and weather, not involving the use of instruments, at synoptic hours as opportunity permits. Trawlers are also equipped for this work, or as Supplementary Ships, whenever appropriate.

Each National Met. Service is responsible for recruiting its own ships. In addition, each Service may recruit ships of other registries which sail regularly from its ports and do not normally return to home ports.

Representatives of Commonwealth and foreign Met. Services regularly co-operate by visiting Selected Ships of other nations to discuss local problems, supply forms, maps or local information, attend instruments, take extracts from logbooks or express appreciation of services rendered. They may also request other ships which are bound to areas where information is sparse, to become Auxiliary Ships on a voyage basis, or to co-operate in particular international projects, such as the recording of deep sea temperatures by expendable bathythermograph. Fleet lists of UK and Commonwealth Selected and Supplementary Ships are published in each July edition of *The Marine Observer*, with updates in the following January.

The World Meteorological Organization. Meteorology being international in character, co-operation between all countries of the world is vital. This was recognized as long ago as 1872 when the International Meteorological Organization (IMO) was formed, which has ever since acted as an advisory body to national Met. Services, its primary functions being the standardization of codes and procedure, the improvement of meteorological practice and the promotion of research. To this last field has been added in recent years studies into the effect of Man's activities on the environment, manifested by the phenomenon of global warming. The Selected Ship scheme and the issue of weather bulletins for shipping on a worldwide basis are co-ordinated by the central body.

The IMO was a semi-official body, and in 1947 it was decided that, in view of the growing importance of meteorology for commercial, economic and scientific purposes, it was necessary to change the status of this organization. As a result an intergovernmental body, the World Meteorological Organization (WMO), held its first congress in Paris during 1951, and assumed the duties and responsibilities of its predecessor. In this organization technical problems are deliberated by a number of technical commissions and working groups, whose members are all experts in their particular sphere. All aspects of maritime meteorology are thus dealt with by the Commission for Marine Meteorology, which advises the WMO as necessary.

Instructions to observers. The instructions to observers issued by the Marine Division of the Met. Office conform to the advice of the WMO. Such changes of codes and procedure as occur from time to time are the result of international agreement. It is inevitable that progress in meteorology should bring changes of

195

procedure. Such changes are kept to a minimum, and the basic aim is that every change should achieve greater worldwide application and uniformity, and hence simplicity. All meteorological work done by ships' officers is entirely voluntary. Only by a voluntary scheme can the requisite high standard of observations be maintained. The benefit of this work to mariners lies in the fact that it forms the basis of the meteorological services for shipping outlined below.

Voluntary observing ships are requested to code and transmit their observations at the standard synoptic hours, namely 0000, 0600, 1200 and 1800 UTC, using the standard International Weather Code, either in full or abbreviated form. Information regarding this code and full instructions for coding are to be found in the *Ships' Code and Decode Book,* (Met.O.509) or in the *Admiralty List of Radio Signals,* Volume 3.

Meteorological services for shipping. The first meteorological service for shipping was the issue of visual Gale Warnings, started in 1861 and suspended in the UK in 1984 as being no longer generally applicable. In 1924, a Radio Weather Shipping Bulletin was instituted; this contained weather reports from certain coastal stations and forecasts for areas around the British Isles. Since then, meteorological warnings of all kinds have been broadcast direct to shipping by radio on an international basis, under arrangements made by the WMO to fulfil the requirements of SOLAS, and more recently by the International Maritime Organization in the form of the Global Maritime Distress and Safety System (GMDSS).

Present-day weather messages to shipping aim to provide not only forecasts but such basic information as will enable simple synoptic charts to be drawn on board ship. Such messages are generally known as bulletins. They usually contain:

Storm warnings.
A brief summary of the weather situation.
Area forecasts.

In addition, the following are sometimes included in the bulletins of certain countries, but are no longer broadcast by the United Kingdom:

Land station reports.
Ships' reports.
Analysis in the International Analysis Code (IAC (Fleet)).

Bulletins. An example of a bulletin is the Atlantic Weather Bulletin, full particulars of which are given in the *Ships' Code and Decode Book,* (Met.O.509), and in *Admiralty List of Radio Signals,* Volume 3. Briefer bulletins for the benefit of coastal shipping are issued by BT coastal radio stations on W/T, R/T, telex, NAVTEX and satellite, and by BBC radio (see brochure *Weather Services for Shipping* obtainable free from the Met. Office).

Facsimile transmissions. The broadcasting of weather maps of many kinds, both synoptic and forecast, by radio facsimile is a valuable facility which is used to reproduce on board ship with the minimum of delay, weather maps drawn by meteorologists ashore. Not only surface weather charts but also wave height, sea-ice and upper-air distribution maps can be received in this way. Installation of the appropriate equipment is, of course, necessary but up-to-date information then becomes readily available with the minimum of trouble. (See also *Meteorology for Mariners*.)

Use of records. The experience of generations of observers is available in the vast number of observations from the oceans that have been collected since 1854. The task of the Marine Division of the Met. Office has been not only to collect these observations but also to classify and analyze them scientifically and to prepare climatological and other material based upon them, for the information of mariners and the world in general. The observations, including those from Ocean Weather Ships of which the UK still operates one vessel in the North Atlantic, are the only surface data regularly available from the oceans. They are put to many other useful purposes and are of great value in research into meteorological problems. Data transmitted from geostationary and polar-orbiting satellites may be improving both in quantity and quality, but they continue to need the verification of ground truth, provided on the oceans by voluntary observing ships.

Data analysis. Analysis is carried out with the aid of the latest computer techniques, including graphics, and the results are published as necessary, after careful assessment by climatological experts, in the form of atlases for the different oceans. The atlases contain mean values for each month of the various meteorological elements observed at sea, and enables the user to assess average conditions at any time in almost any part of the world. One of the most recent atlases, published by the Met. Office in 1990, is the *Global Ocean Surface Temperature Atlas*, a climatology of global sea surface temperature, based on observations for the period 1951–80, and owing much to the perseverance and dedication of the many 'unknown mariners' whose observations contributed much of the data.

Guidance for the conduct of the work at sea. Direct contact between the Met. Office and ships' masters and observers is maintained through Port Met. Officers in the UK based at Cardiff, Greenock, Hull, Liverpool, London (at Grays near Tilbury), Middlesbrough and Southampton. Contact may also be made with Port Met. Officers in many ports overseas; details for these ports are listed in Met.O.477A, *Marine Observer's Guide*, and in certain nautical almanacs and other publications.

Indirect contact with the Voluntary Observing Fleet is maintained through the medium of *The Marine Observer*, a quarterly publication containing articles on meteorology, oceanography, ice and related subjects of interest to seamen. A large section of the journal is devoted to observations of meteorological and biological phenomena extracted from the meteorological logbooks of ships of the UK and the British Commonwealth.

Instruments are supplied to ships by Port Met. Officers in the UK when possible, or by selected Port Met. Officers overseas who hold stocks on behalf of the UK, and are delivered by hand whenever practicable. When it is desired to return instruments lent by the Met. Office, and at any time when the ship is to change owners or managers, with a corresponding change in manning, the Met. Office or an appropriate Port Met. Officer should be advised. When this is not possible, as for example at ports overseas, application should be made to the Marine Superintendent of the Met. Office for instructions. Similar remarks apply to the return of damaged instruments for repair or replacement.

Any accident to an instrument, even though no apparent damage is done, should be reported to a Port Met. Officer. This is necessary because the constants of the instrument may have been altered without any apparent difference in its working. On no account should a barometer or any other instrument belonging to the Met. Office be sent to an instrument maker for repair or any attempt be made to repair the instrument on board the ship.

CHAPTER 14

THE INTERNATIONAL CONVENTION FOR THE SAFETY OF LIFE AT SEA, 1974*

Upon the invitation of the International Maritime Organization, a Conference was held in London in October 1974 for the purpose of drawing up a Convention to replace the International Convention for the Safety of Life at Sea (SOLAS) signed in London in 1960, which itself replaced the previous Convention of 1948.

This Conference took cognizance of the mariners' requirements for meteorological information and their ability to detect and warn others of hazardous conditions. The following regulations were therefore included in the SOLAS convention, chapter V — Safety of Navigation.

REGULATION 2: *Danger Messages*

(a) The Master of every ship which meets with dangerous ice, a dangerous derelict, or any other direct danger to navigation, or a tropical storm, or encounters sub-freezing air temperatures associated with gale force winds causing severe ice accretion on superstructures, or winds of force 10 or above on the Beaufort Scale for which no storm warning has been received, is bound to communicate the information by all the means at his disposal to ships in the vicinity, and also to the competent authorities at the first point on the coast with which he can communicate. The form in which the information is sent is not obligatory. It may be transmitted either in plain language (preferably English) or by means of the International Code of Signals. It should be broadcast to all ships in the vicinity and sent to the first point on the coast to which communication can be made, with a request that it be transmitted to the appropriate authorities.

(b) Each Contracting Government will take steps necessary to ensure that when intelligence of any of the dangers specified in paragraph (a) is received, it will be promptly brought to the knowledge of those concerned and communicated to other interested Governments.

(c) The transmission of messages respecting the dangers specified is free of cost to the ships concerned.

(d) All radio messages issued under paragraph (a) of this Regulation shall be preceded by the Safety Signal, using the signal as prescribed by the Radio Regulations as defined in Regulation 2 of Chapter IV.

---

*See *International Convention for the Safety of Life at Sea*, 1974, its Protocol of 1978 and subsequent amendments, IMO, London.

REGULATION 3:   *Information required in danger messages*

The following information is required in danger messages:

(a)   Ice, derelicts and other direct dangers to navigation.
   (i)   the kind of ice, derelict or danger observed;
   (ii)   the position of the ice, derelict or danger when last observed;
   (iii)   the time and date (UTC) when danger last observed.
(b)   Tropical Storms.*
   (i)   A statement that a tropical storm has been encountered. This obligation should be interpreted in a broad spirit, and information transmitted whenever the master has a good reason to believe that a tropical storm is developing or exists in his neighbourhood.
   (ii)   Time, date (UTC) and position of ship when the observation was taken.
   (iii)   As much of the following information as is practicable should be included in the message:
      — barometric pressure, preferably corrected (stating millibars, millimetres or inches, and whether corrected or uncorrected);
      — barometric tendency (the change in barometric pressure during the past three hours);
      — true wind direction;
      — wind force (Beaufort scale);
      — state of the sea (smooth, moderate, rough, high);
      — swell (slight, moderate, heavy) and the true direction from which it comes. Period or length of swell (short, average, long) would also be of value;
      — true course and speed of ship.
(c)   Subsequent Observations. When a master has reported a tropical or other dangerous storm, it is desirable, but not obligatory, that further observations be made and transmitted hourly, if practicable, but in any case at intervals of not more than three hours, so long as the ship remains under the influence of the storm.
(d)   Winds of force 10 or above on the Beaufort Scale for which no storm warning has been received.
   This is intended to deal with storms other than the tropical storms referred to in paragraph (b); when such a storm is encountered, the message should contain similar information to that listed under paragraph (b) but excluding the details concerning sea and swell.
(e)   Sub-freezing air temperatures associated with gale force winds causing severe ice accretion on superstructures.
   (i)   Time and date (UTC).
   (ii)   Air temperature.
   (iii)   Sea temperature (if practicable).
   (iv)   Wind force and direction.

*Tropical cyclone is the commonest generic term used by the National Met. Services. The terms hurricane, typhoon, severe cyclonic storm, etc. are also used, depending on geographic location and with particular reference to the most severe storms.

EXAMPLES

Ice

TTT Ice. Large berg sighted in 4605N, 4410W, at 0800 UTC, May 15.

Derelicts

TTT Derelict. Observed derelict almost submerged in 4006N, 1243W, at 1630 UTC, April 21.

Danger to Navigation

TTT Navigation. Alpha lightship not on station. 1800 UTC. January 3.

Tropical Storm

TTT Storm. 0030 UTC. August 18. 2204N, 11354E. Barometer corrected 994 millibars, tendency down 6 millibars. Wind NW, force 9, heavy squalls. Heavy easterly swell. Course 067, 5 knots.

TTT Storm. Appearances indicate approach of hurricane. 1300 UTC. September 14. 2200N, 7236W. Barometer corrected 1004 millibars, tendency down 4 millibars. Wind NE, force 8, frequent rain squalls. Course 035, 9 knots.

TTT Storm. Conditions indicate intense cyclone has formed. 0200 UTC. May 4, 1620N, 9203E. Barometer uncorrected 998 millibars, tendency down 5 millibars. Wind S by W, force 5. Course 300, 8 knots.

TTT Storm. Typhoon to southeast 0300 UTC. June 12. 1812N, 12605E. Barometer falling rapidly. Wind increasing from N.

TTT Storm. Wind force 11, no storm warning received. 0300 UTC. May 4. 4830N, 30W. Barometer corrected 983 millibars, tendency down 4 millibars. Wind SW, force 11 veering. Course 260, 6 knots.

Icing

TTT Experiencing severe icing. 1400 UTC. March 2. 69N, 10W. Air temperature minus 8°C. Sea temperature minus 2°C. Wind NE, force 8.

REGULATION 4: *Meteorological Services*

(a) The Contracting Governments undertake to encourage the collection of meteorological data by ships at sea and to arrange for their examination, dissemination and exchange in the manner most suitable for the purpose of aiding navigation. Administrations shall encourage the use of instruments of a high degree of accuracy, and shall facilitate the checking of such instruments upon request.

(b) In particular, the Contracting Governments undertake to co-operate in carrying out, as far as practicable, the following meteorological arrangements:

(i) To warn ships of gales, storms and tropical storms, both by the issue of radio messages and by the display of appropriate signals at coastal points.

(ii) To issue daily, by radio, weather bulletins suitable for shipping, containing data of existing weather, waves and ice, forecasts, and when practicable, sufficient additional information to enable simple weather charts to be prepared at sea and also to encourage the transmission of suitable facsimile weather charts.

(iii) To prepare and issue such publications as may be necessary for the efficient conduct of meteorological work at sea and to arrange, if practicable, for the publication and making available of daily weather charts for the information of departing ships.

(iv) To arrange for selected ships to be equipped with tested instruments (such as a barometer, a barograph, a psychrometer, and suitable apparatus for measuring sea temperature) for use in this service, and to take meteorological observations at main standard times for surface synoptic observations (at least four times daily, whenever circumstances permit) and to encourage other ships to take observations in a modified form, particularly when in areas where shipping is sparse; these ships to transmit their observations by radio for the benefit of the various official meteorological services, repeating the information for the benefit of ships in the vicinity. When in the vicinity of a tropical storm, or of a suspected tropical storm, ships should be encouraged to take and transmit their observations at more frequent intervals whenever practicable, bearing in mind navigational pre-occupations of ships' officers during storm conditions.

(v) To arrange for the reception and transmission by coast radio stations of weather messages from and to ships. Ships which are unable to communicate direct with shore shall be encouraged to relay their weather messages through ocean weather ships or through other ships which are in contact with shore.

(vi) To encourage all masters to inform ships in the vicinity and also shore stations whenever they experience a wind speed of 50 knots or more (force 10 on the Beaufort scale).

(vii) To endeavour to obtain a uniform procedure in regard to the international meteorological services already specified, and, as far as is practicable, to conform to the Technical Regulations and recommendations made by the World Meteorological Organization, to which the Contracting Governments may refer for study and advice any meteorological question which may arise in carrying out the present Convention.

(c) The information provided for in this Regulation shall be furnished in form for transmission and transmitted in the order of priority prescribed by the Radio Regulations, and during transmission 'to all stations' of meteorological information, forecasts and warnings, all ship stations must conform to the provisions of the Radio Regulations.

(d) Forecasts, warnings, synoptic and other meteorological reports intended for ships shall be issued and disseminated by the national service in the best position to serve various zones and areas, in accordance with mutual arrangements made by the Contracting Governments concerned.

Tables

TABLE 1 — *Correction of millibar barometers to mean sea level*

These corrections are to be **added** to the barometer readings

Height	Temperature of Air (°C) (Dry bulb in screen)											
	−15	−10	−5	0	5	10	15	20	25	30	35	40
metres					*millibars*							
5	0.7	0.6	0.6	0.6	0.6	0.6	0.6	0.6	0.6	0.6	0.6	0.5
10	1.3	1.3	1.3	1.3	1.2	1.2	1.2	1.2	1.1	1.1	1.1	1.1
15	2.0	1.9	1.9	1.9	1.8	1.8	1.8	1.7	1.7	1.7	1.7	1.6
20	2.6	2.6	2.5	2.5	2.5	2.4	2.4	2.3	2.3	2.3	2.2	2.2
25	3.3	3.2	3.2	3.1	3.1	3.0	3.0	2.9	2.9	2.8	2.8	2.7
30	4.0	3.9	3.8	3.8	3.7	3.6	3.6	3.5	3.4	3.4	3.3	3.3
35	4.6	4.5	4.5	4.4	4.3	4.2	4.2	4.1	4.0	3.9	3.9	3.8
40	5.3	5.2	5.1	5.0	4.9	4.8	4.7	4.7	4.6	4.5	4.4	4.4
45	6.0	5.9	5.7	5.6	5.5	5.4	5.3	5.3	5.2	5.1	5.0	4.9
50	6.6	6.5	6.4	6.3	6.2	6.0	5.9	5.8	5.7	5.6	5.6	5.5

THE DIURNAL VARIATION OF BAROMETRIC PRESSURE IN THE ZONES OF LATITUDE 0–10° AND 10–20°, N OR S

TABLE 2 — Correction to be applied to the observed pressure for diurnal variation			TABLE 3 — Average values of barometric change in an hour due to diurnal variation		

Local Time	0–10° N or S	10–20° N or S	Local Time	0–10° N or S	10–20° N or S
	mb	mb		mb	mb
0	−0.6	−0.5	0–1	−0.5	−0.4
1	−0.1	−0.1	1–2	−0.4	−0.4
2	+0.3	+0.3	2–3	−0.4	−0.4
3	+0.7	+0.7	3–4	−0.1	−0.1
4	+0.8	+0.8	4–5	+0.2	+0.2
5	+0.6	+0.6	5–6	+0.4	+0.4
6	+0.2	+0.2	6–7	+0.6	+0.5
7	−0.4	−0.3	7–8	+0.5	+0.5
8	−0.9	−0.8	8–9	+0.4	+0.3
9	−1.3	−1.1	9–10	+0.1	+0.1
10	−1.4	−1.2	10–11	−0.3	−0.2
11	−1.1	−1.0	11–12	−0.5	−0.5
12	−0.6	−0.5	12–13	−0.7	−0.6
13	+0.1	+0.1	13–14	−0.6	−0.6
14	+0.7	+0.7	14–15	−0.6	−0.4
15	+1.3	+1.1	15–16	−0.2	−0.2
16	+1.5	+1.3	16–17	+0.1	+0.1
17	+1.4	+1.2	17–18	+0.4	+0.3
18	+1.0	+0.9	18–19	+0.5	+0.6
19	+0.5	+0.3	19–20	+0.6	+0.5
20	−0.1	−0.2	20–21	+0.5	+0.4
21	−0.6	−0.6	21–22	+0.3	+0.2
22	−0.9	−0.8	22–23	0	0
23	−0.9	−0.8	23–24	−0.3	−0.3
24	−0.6	−0.5			

These tables are based on observations made in British ships, at the hours 0000, 0400, 0800, 1200, 1600, 2000 local time, between the years 1919–1938.

In the tropics, should the barometer, after correction for diurnal variation (Table 2), be as much as 3 millibars below the monthly normal for the locality, as shown on meteorological charts, the mariner should be on the alert, as there is a distinct possibility that a tropical storm has formed, or is forming. A comparison of subsequent hourly changes in his barometer with the corresponding figures in Table 3 will show whether these changes indicate a real further fall in pressure and, if so, its amount.

Caution. When entering a barometric pressure in the log the correction for diurnal variation must not be applied.

TABLE 4 — *Dew-point (°C)*
(For use with marine screen)

Dry Bulb °C	Depression of Wet Bulb																									Dry Bulb °C
	0°	0.2°	0.4°	0.6°	0.8°	1.0°	1.2°	1.4°	1.6°	1.8°	2.0°	2.5°	3.0°	3.5°	4.0°	4.5°	5.0°	5.5°	6.0°	6.5°	7.0°	7.5°	8.0°	8.5°	9.0°	°C
40	40	40	40	39	39	39	39	38	38	38	38	37	36	36	35	34	34	33	32	32	31	30	29	29	28	40
39	39	39	39	38	38	38	38	37	37	37	37	36	35	35	34	33	33	32	31	31	30	29	28	28	27	39
38	38	38	38	37	37	37	37	36	36	36	35	35	34	34	33	32	32	31	30	29	29	28	27	26	26	38
37	37	37	37	36	36	36	36	35	35	35	34	34	33	32	32	31	31	30	29	28	28	27	26	25	24	37
36	36	36	35	35	35	35	34	34	34	34	33	33	32	31	31	30	30	29	28	27	26	26	25	24	23	36
35	35	35	34	34	34	34	33	33	33	33	32	32	31	30	30	29	29	28	27	26	25	24	24	23	22	35
34	34	34	33	33	33	33	32	32	32	32	31	31	30	29	29	28	27	27	26	25	24	23	22	22	21	34
33	33	33	32	32	32	32	31	31	31	31	30	30	29	28	28	27	26	26	25	24	23	22	21	20	19	33
32	32	32	31	31	31	31	30	30	30	30	29	29	28	27	27	26	25	25	24	23	22	21	20	19	18	32
31	31	31	30	30	30	30	29	29	29	29	28	28	27	26	26	25	24	24	23	22	21	20	19	18	17	31
30	30	30	29	29	29	29	28	28	28	28	27	27	26	25	25	24	23	22	21	20	19	18	18	17	16	30
29	29	29	28	28	28	28	27	27	27	27	26	25	25	24	23	22	22	21	20	19	18	17	16	15	14	29
28	28	28	27	27	27	27	26	26	26	25	25	24	24	23	22	21	20	20	19	18	17	16	15	14	13	28
27	27	27	27	26	26	26	25	25	25	24	24	23	23	22	21	20	19	18	18	17	16	15	14	13	11	27
26	26	26	25	25	25	25	24	24	23	23	23	22	22	21	20	19	18	17	16	16	15	14	13	11	10	26
25	25	25	24	24	24	24	23	23	23	22	22	21	20	20	19	18	17	16	15	14	13	12	11	10	8	25
24	24	24	23	23	23	23	22	22	22	21	21	20	19	19	18	17	16	15	14	13	12	11	10	8	7	24
23	23	23	22	22	22	21	21	21	21	20	20	19	18	17	17	16	15	14	13	12	11	9	8	7	5	23
22	22	22	21	21	21	20	20	20	20	19	19	18	17	16	15	14	13	12	11	10	9	8	6	5	3	22
21	21	21	20	20	20	19	19	19	19	18	18	18	17	16	15	14	13	12	11	10	9	8	7	3	1	21
20	20	20	19	19	19	18	18	18	17	17	17	16	15	14	13	12	11	10	9	9	8	6	6	1	0	20
19	19	19	18	18	18	17	17	17	16	16	16	15	14	13	12	11	10	9	7	6	4	3	1	0	-2	19
18	18	18	17	17	17	16	16	16	15	15	15	14	13	12	11	10	8	7	6	4	3	1	-0	-2	-5	18
17	17	17	16	16	16	15	15	15	14	14	14	13	12	11	9	8	7	6	4	3	1	-0	-3	-5	-7	17
16	16	16	15	15	15	14	14	14	13	13	12	11	10	9	8	7	6	4	3	1	0	-2	-5	-7	-10	16
15	15	15	14	14	14	13	13	12	12	12	11	10	9	8	7	6	4	3	1	0	-2	-5	-7	-10	-14	15
14	14	14	13	13	13	12	12	11	11	11	10	9	8	7	6	4	3	1	0	-2	-4	-7	-10	-13	-18	14
13	13	13	12	12	11	11	11	10	10	10	9	8	7	6	4	3	1	0	-2	-4	-7	-9	-13	-17	-23	13
12	12	12	11	11	10	10	10	10	9	9	9	7	6	4	3	1	-0	-2	-4	-6	-9	-12	-16	-22	-33	12
11	11	11	10	10	10	9	9	9	8	8	8	7	5	4	3	1	-2	-4	-6	-8	-12	-15	-21	-30		11
10	10	10	9	9	9	8	8	8	7	7	6	6	4	3	2	0	-3	-6	-8	-11	-15	-19	-27			10

TABLE 4 — (contd)

Dry Bulb °C	0°	0.2°	0.4°	0.6°	0.8°	1.0°	1.2°	1.4°	1.6°	1.8°	2.0°	2.5°	3.0°	3.5°	4.0°	4.5°	5.0°	5.5°	6.0°	6.5°	7.0°	Dry Bulb °C
								Depression of Wet Bulb														
9	9	9	8	8	7	7	6	6	5	5	4	3	2	0	−1	−3	−5	−8	−10	−14	−18	9
8	8	8	7	7	6	6	5	5	4	4	3	2	0	−1	−3	−5	−7	−10	−13	−17		8
7	7	7	6	6	5	5	4	4	3	3	2	1	−1	−3	−4	−7	−9	−12	−16			7
6	6	6	5	5	4	4	3	3	2	2	1	−0	−2	−4	−6	−9	−11	−15				6
5	5	5	4	4	3	3	2	2	1	1	0	−2	−4	−6	−8	−10	−14	−18				5
4	4	4	3	3	2	2	1	0	0	−1	−1	−3	−5	−7	−10	−11	−14					4
3	3	3	2	2	1	1	0	−1	−1	−2	−3	−5	−7	−8	−11	−14	−17					3
2	2	2	1	0	0	0	−1	−2	−2	−3	−3	−5	−8	−10	−13	−16						2
1	1	1	0	−1	−1	−2	−2	−3	−3	−4	−4	−7	−9	−12	−15	−19						1
0	0	−1	−1	−2	−2	−3	−4	−4	−5	−6	−7	−9	−11	−14	−18							0
−1	−1	−2	−2	−3	−4	−4	−5	−6	−6	−7	−8	−10	−13	−17								
−2	−2	−3	−4	−4	−5	−6	−6	−7	−8	−9	−10	−12	−15	−19								
−3	−3	−4	−5	−5	−6	−7	−8	−9	−9	−10	−11	−14	−18									
−4	−4	−5	−6	−7	−8	−8	−9	−10	−11	−12	−13	−16										
−5	−5	−6	−7	−8	−9	−10	−11	−11	−13	−14	−15	−18										
−6	−6	−7	−8	−9	−10	−11	−12	−13	−14	−15	−17											
−7	−7	−9	−9	−10	−11	−12	−13	−15	−16	−17	−19											
−8	−8	−10	−10	−12	−13	−14	−15	−16	−17	−19												
−9	−9	−11	−11	−13	−14	−15	−16	−18	−19													
−10	−11	−12	−13	−14	−15	−17	−18															
−11	−12	−13	−14	−16	−17	−18																
−12	−13	−14	−16	−17	−18																	
−13	−15	−16	−17	−18																		
−14	−16	−17	−18																			
−15	−17	−18																				
−16	−18																					
−17	−19																					

In the tables, lines are ruled to draw attention to the fact that above the line evaporation is going on from a water surface, while below the line it is going on from an ice surface. Owing to this, interpolation must not be made between figures on different sides of the lines.

For dry bulb temperatures below 0°C it will be noticed that, when the depression of the wet bulb is zero, i.e. when the temperature of the wet bulb is equal to that of the dry bulb, the dew-point is still below the dry bulb, and the relative humidity is less than 100 per cent. These apparent anomalies are a consequence of the method of computing dew-points and relative humidities now adopted by the Met. Office, in which the standard saturation pressure for temperatures below 0°C is taken as that over water, and not as that over Ice.

TABLE 5 — *Dew-point* (°C)

(For use with aspirated psychrometer)

Dry Bulb °C	Depression of Wet Bulb																			Dry Bulb °C
	0°	0.5°	1.0°	1.5°	2.0°	2.5°	3.0°	3.5°	4.0°	4.5°	5.0°	5.5°	6.0°	6.5°	7.0°	7.5°	8.0°	8.5°	9.0°	
40	40	39	39	38	38	37	36	36	35	35	34	33	33	32	31	31	30	29	29	40
39	39	38	38	37	37	36	35	35	34	33	33	32	32	31	30	29	29	28	27	39
38	38	37	37	36	36	35	34	34	33	32	32	31	30	30	29	28	28	27	26	38
37	37	36	36	35	35	34	33	33	32	31	31	30	29	29	28	27	27	26	25	37
36	36	35	35	34	34	33	32	32	31	30	30	29	28	28	27	26	25	25	24	36
35	35	34	34	33	33	32	31	31	30	29	29	28	27	26	26	25	24	24	23	35
34	34	33	33	32	31	31	30	30	29	28	28	27	26	25	25	24	23	22	22	34
33	33	32	32	31	30	30	29	28	28	27	26	26	25	24	23	23	22	22	20	33
32	32	31	31	30	29	29	28	27	27	26	25	25	24	23	22	22	21	21	19	32
31	31	30	30	29	28	28	27	26	26	25	24	24	23	22	21	20	20	19	18	31
30	30	29	29	28	27	27	26	25	25	24	23	22	22	21	20	19	18	17	17	30
29	29	28	28	27	26	26	25	24	24	23	22	21	20	20	19	18	17	16	15	29
28	28	27	27	26	25	25	24	23	22	22	21	20	19	19	18	17	16	15	14	28
27	27	26	26	25	24	24	23	22	21	21	20	19	18	17	16	16	15	14	13	27
26	26	25	25	24	23	23	22	21	20	19	19	18	17	16	15	14	13	12	11	26
25	25	24	24	23	22	21	21	20	19	18	18	17	16	15	14	13	12	11	10	25
24	24	23	23	22	21	20	20	19	18	17	16	16	15	14	13	12	11	10	8	24
23	23	22	22	21	20	19	19	18	17	16	15	14	13	12	11	10	9	8	7	23
22	22	21	21	20	19	18	17	17	16	15	14	13	12	11	10	9	8	7	5	22
21	21	20	20	19	18	17	16	16	15	14	13	12	11	10	9	8	6	5	4	21
20	20	19	19	18	17	16	15	14	14	13	12	11	10	9	7	6	5	4	2	20
19	19	18	17	17	16	15	14	13	12	11	10	9	8	7	6	5	3	2	0	19
18	18	17	16	16	15	14	13	12	11	10	9	8	7	6	5	3	2	0	−1	18
17	17	16	15	15	14	13	12	11	10	9	8	7	6	4	3	2	0	−2	−3	17
16	16	15	14	14	13	12	11	10	9	8	7	5	4	3	2	0	−2	−4	−6	16
15	15	14	13	13	12	11	10	9	8	7	5	4	3	1	0	−2	−4	−6	−8	15
14	14	13	12	12	11	10	9	7	6	5	4	3	1	0	−2	−4	−6	−8	−11	14
13	13	12	11	11	10	9	7	6	5	4	3	1	0	−2	−4	−6	−8	−11	−14	13
12	12	11	10	10	9	8	6	5	4	3	1	0	−2	−4	−6	−8	−10	−13	−17	12
11	11	10	9	9	8	7	5	4	3	1	0	−2	−3	−5	−8	−10	−13	−17	−22	11
10	10	9	8	7	6	5	4	3	1	0	−2	−3	−5	−7	−10	−13	−16	−21	−29	10

TABLE 5 — (contd)

Dry Bulb °C	0°	0.5°	1.0°	1.5°	2.0°	2.5°	3.0°	3.5°	4.0°	4.5°	5.0°	5.5°	6.0°	6.5°	7.0°	7.5°	8.0°	8.5°	9.0°	Dry Bulb °C
9	9	8	7	6	5	4	3	1	0	-2	-3	-5	-7	-9	-12	-16	-20	-27	-45	9
8	8	7	6	5	4	3	1	0	-2	-3	-5	-7	-9	-12	-15	-19	-25	-25	-36	8
7	7	6	5	4	3	1	0	-1	-3	-5	-7	-9	-11	-14	-18	-19	-24	-34		7
6	6	5	4	3	1	0	-1	-3	-4	-6	-8	-11	-14	-14	-18	-23	-32			6
5	5	4	3	2	0	-1	-3	-4	-6	-8	-10	-11	-14	-18	-22	-30				5
4	4	3	2	0	-1	-2	-4	-6	-8	-9	-11	-14	-17	-22	-28	-45				4
3	3	2	1	-1	-2	-4	-5	-6	-8	-11	-13	-16	-21	-27	-39					3
2	2	1	0	-2	-3	-4	-6	-8	-10	-13	-16	-20	-25	-34						2
1	1	0	-2	-3	-4	-6	-8	-10	-12	-15	-19	-24	-31							1
0	0	-1	-3	-4	-6	-8	-9	-12	-14	-18	-22	-29	-44							0
-1	-1	-2	-4	-5	-7	-9	-11	-14	-17	-21	-26	-37								
-2	-2	-4	-5	-7	-9	-11	-13	-16	-19	-24	-32									
-3	-3	-5	-6	-8	-10	-12	-15	-18	-23	-29	-44									
-4	-4	-6	-8	-10	-12	-14	-17	-21	-26	-36										
-5	-5	-7	-9	-11	-13	-16	-19	-24	-31											
-6	-6	-8	-10	-13	-15	-18	-22	-28	-39											
-7	-7	-10	-12	-14	-17	-20	-25	-32												
-8	-8	-11	-13	-16	-19	-23	-28	-40												
-9	-9	-12	-14	-17	-21	-25	-33													
-10	-10	-13	-16	-19	-23	-28	-39													
-11	-11	-15	-17	-21	-25	-32														
-12	-12	-16	-19	-23	-28	-38														
-13	-13	-17	-20	-25	-31	-47														
-14	-14	-18	-22	-27	-35															
-15	-15	-20	-24	-29	-40															
-16	-16	-21	-25	-32																
-17	-17	-22	-27	-35																

Depression of Wet Bulb

See footnotes to Table 4

209

TABLE 6 — *Relative Humidity (per cent)*

(For use with marine screen)

Dry Bulb °C	Depression of Wet Bulb																								Dry Bulb °C
°C	0.2°	0.4°	0.6°	0.8°	1.0°	1.2°	1.4°	1.6°	1.8°	2.0°	2.5°	3.0°	3.5°	4.0°	4.5°	5.0°	5.5°	6.0°	6.5°	7.0°	7.5°	8.0°	8.5°	9.0°	°C
40	99	97	96	95	94	92	91	90	89	88	85	82	79	76	73	71	68	66	63	61	58	56	53	51	40
39	99	97	96	95	94	92	91	90	89	87	84	82	79	76	73	70	68	65	63	60	58	55	53	50	39
38	99	97	96	95	94	92	91	90	89	87	84	81	78	75	73	70	67	65	62	59	57	54	52	50	38
37	99	97	96	95	93	92	91	90	88	87	84	81	78	75	72	69	67	64	61	59	56	54	51	49	37
36	99	97	96	95	93	92	91	90	88	87	84	81	78	75	72	69	66	63	61	58	55	53	50	48	36
35	99	97	96	95	93	92	91	89	88	87	83	80	77	74	71	68	65	63	60	57	55	52	49	47	35
34	99	97	96	94	93	92	91	89	88	86	83	80	76	74	71	68	65	63	59	56	54	51	49	46	34
33	99	97	96	94	93	91	90	89	87	86	83	80	76	73	71	68	65	62	58	56	53	50	48	45	33
32	99	97	96	94	93	91	90	89	87	86	83	79	76	73	70	67	64	61	58	55	52	49	47	44	32
31	99	97	96	94	93	91	90	89	87	86	82	79	75	72	69	66	64	61	57	54	51	48	46	43	31
30	98	97	95	94	93	91	90	88	87	85	82	78	75	72	68	65	62	59	56	53	50	47	44	42	30
29	98	97	95	94	92	91	89	88	86	85	81	78	74	71	68	65	61	58	55	52	49	46	43	40	29
28	98	97	95	94	92	91	89	88	86	85	81	77	74	70	67	64	60	57	54	51	48	45	42	39	28
27	98	97	95	94	92	90	89	87	86	84	81	77	73	70	66	63	60	56	53	50	47	44	41	38	27
26	98	97	95	93	92	90	89	87	86	84	80	76	73	69	66	62	59	55	52	49	46	42	39	36	26
25	98	97	95	93	92	90	88	87	85	84	80	76	72	68	65	61	58	54	51	47	44	41	38	35	25
24	98	97	95	93	91	90	88	86	85	83	79	75	71	68	64	60	57	53	50	46	43	39	36	33	24
23	98	96	95	93	91	89	88	86	84	83	79	75	71	67	63	59	56	52	48	45	41	38	35	31	23
22	98	96	95	93	91	89	88	86	84	82	78	74	70	66	62	58	54	51	47	43	40	36	33	29	22
21	98	96	94	93	91	89	87	85	84	82	78	73	69	65	61	57	53	49	45	42	38	34	31	27	21
20	98	96	94	92	91	89	87	85	83	81	77	73	68	64	60	56	52	48	44	40	36	33	29	25	20
19	98	96	94	92	90	88	86	85	83	81	76	72	67	63	59	55	50	46	42	38	34	31	27	23	19
18	98	96	94	92	90	88	86	84	82	80	76	71	66	62	58	53	49	45	41	36	32	28	25	21	18
17	98	96	94	92	90	88	86	84	82	80	75	70	65	61	56	52	47	43	39	34	30	26	22	18	17
16	98	96	94	91	89	87	85	83	81	79	74	69	64	60	55	50	46	41	37	32	28	24	20	16	16
15	98	96	93	91	89	87	85	83	81	79	73	68	63	58	53	49	44	39	35	30	26	21	17	13	15
14	98	95	93	91	89	86	84	82	80	78	72	67	62	57	52	47	42	37	32	28	23	18	14	10	14
13	98	95	93	91	88	86	84	81	79	77	71	66	61	55	50	45	40	35	30	25	20	16	11	6	13
12	98	95	93	90	88	86	83	81	78	76	70	65	59	54	48	43	38	32	27	22	17	12	8	3	12
11	97	95	92	90	87	85	83	80	78	75	69	63	58	52	46	41	35	30	25	19	14	9	4		11
10	97	95	92	90	87	84	82	79	77	74	68	62	56	50	44	38	33	27	22	16	11	5			10

210

TABLE 6 — (contd)

Dry Bulb °C	Depression of Wet Bulb																					
	0.2°	0.4°	0.6°	0.8°	1.0°	1.2°	1.4°	1.6°	1.8°	2.0°	2.5°	3.0°	3.5°	4.0°	4.5°	5.0°	5.5°	6.0°	6.5°	7.0°	7.5°	8.0°
9	97	95	92	89	86	84	81	79	76	73	67	61	54	48	42	36	30	24	18	13	7	2
8	97	94	92	89	86	83	80	78	75	72	66	59	52	46	40	33	27	21	15	9	3	
7	97	94	91	88	85	82	80	77	74	71	64	57	50	44	37	31	24	18	11	5	5	
6	97	94	91	88	85	82	79	76	73	70	63	55	48	41	34	28	21	14	13	6		
5	97	94	90	87	84	81	78	75	72	69	61	53	46	39	31	24	22	15	8	2		
4	97	93	90	87	84	80	77	74	70	67	59	51	44	36	32	25	18	10	3			
3	96	93	89	86	83	79	76	72	69	66	57	49	44	36	28	21	14	6				
2	96	93	89	85	82	78	75	71	67	64	58	49	41	33	24	16	9	1				
1	96	92	88	85	81	78	75	71	67	64	55	46	37	29	20	12	3					
0	96	92	88	84	80	76	73	69	65	61	52	43	33	24	16	7						
−1	95	91	87	83	78	74	70	66	62	58	49	39	29	20	11	1						
−2	94	89	85	81	77	72	68	64	60	56	45	35	25	15	5							
−3	93	88	84	79	75	70	66	61	57	53	42	31	21	10								
−4	91	87	82	77	72	68	63	59	54	49	38	27	16	5								
−5	90	85	80	75	70	65	61	56	51	46	34	22	11									
−6	89	84	79	73	68	63	58	53	48	42	30	17	5									
−7	88	82	77	71	66	60	55	49	44	39	25	12										
−8	87	81	75	69	63	57	52	46	40	35	20	6										
−9	85	79	73	67	61	54	48	42	36	30	15											
−10	84	77	71	64	58	51	45	38	32	26												
−11	83	76	69	62	55	48	41	34	27	21												
−12	81	74	67	59	52	44	37	30	22	15												
−13	80	72	64	56	48	41	33	25	17	9												
−14	79	70	62	53	45	36	28	20	11	3												
−15	77	68	59	50	41	32	23	14	5													
−16	76	66	56	47	37	27	18	8														
−17	74	64	53	43	33	22	12	2														

In the tables, lines are ruled to draw attention to the fact that above the line evaporation is going on from a water surface, while below the line it is going on from an ice surface (wet-bulb temperature 0°C). Owing to this, interpolation must not be made between figures on different sides of the line.

TABLE 7 — *Conversion of temperature readings on the Celsius scale to the Fahrenheit and kelvin scales*

°C	°F	K	°C	°F	K	°C	°F	K
−25.0	−13.0	248.15	0.0	+32.0	273.15	+25.0	+77.0	298.15
−24.5	−12.1	248.65	+0.5	32.9	273.65	25.5	77.9	298.65
−24.0	−11.2	249.15	1.0	33.8	274.15	26.0	78.8	299.15
−23.5	−10.3	249.65	1.5	34.7	274.65	26.5	79.7	299.65
−23.0	−9.4	250.15	2.0	35.6	275.15	27.0	80.6	300.15
−22.5	−8.5	250.65	2.5	36.5	275.65	27.5	81.5	300.65
−22.0	−7.6	251.15	3.0	37.4	276.15	28.0	82.4	301.15
−21.5	−6.7	251.65	3.5	38.3	276.65	28.5	83.3	301.65
−21.0	−5.8	252.15	4.0	39.2	277.15	29.0	84.2	302.15
−20.5	−4.9	252.65	4.5	40.1	277.65	29.5	85.1	302.65
−20.0	−4.0	253.15	5.0	41.0	278.15	30.0	86.0	303.15
−19.5	−3.1	253.65	5.5	41.9	278.65	30.5	86.9	303.65
−19.0	−2.2	254.15	6.0	42.8	279.15	31.0	87.8	304.15
−18.5	−1.3	254.65	6.5	43.7	279.65	31.5	88.7	304.65
−18.0	−0.4	255.15	7.0	44.6	280.15	32.0	89.6	305.15
−17.5	+0.5	255.65	7.5	45.5	280.65	32.5	90.5	305.65
−17.0	1.4	256.15	8.0	46.4	281.15	33.0	91.4	306.15
−16.5	2.3	256.65	8.5	47.3	281.65	33.5	92.3	306.65
−16.0	3.2	257.15	9.0	48.2	282.15	34.0	93.2	307.15
−15.5	4.1	257.65	9.5	49.1	282.65	34.5	94.1	307.65
−15.0	5.0	258.15	10.0	50.0	283.15	35.0	95.0	308.15
−14.5	5.9	258.65	10.5	50.9	283.65	35.5	95.9	308.65
−14.0	6.8	259.15	11.0	51.8	284.15	36.0	96.8	309.15
−13.5	7.7	259.65	11.5	52.7	284.65	36.5	97.7	309.65
−13.0	8.6	260.15	12.0	53.6	285.15	37.0	98.6	310.15
−12.5	9.5	260.65	12.5	54.5	285.65	37.5	99.5	310.65
−12.0	10.4	261.15	13.0	55.4	286.15	38.0	100.4	311.15
−11.5	11.3	261.65	13.5	56.3	286.65	38.5	101.3	311.65
−11.2	12.2	262.15	14.0	57.2	287.15	39.0	102.2	312.15
−10.5	13.1	262.65	14.5	58.1	287.65	39.5	103.1	312.65
−10.0	14.0	263.15	15.0	59.0	288.15	40.0	104.0	313.15
−9.5	14.9	263.65	15.5	59.9	288.65	40.5	104.9	313.65
−9.0	15.8	264.15	16.0	60.8	289.15	41.0	105.8	314.15
−8.5	16.7	264.65	16.5	61.7	289.65	41.5	106.7	314.65
−8.0	17.6	265.15	17.0	62.6	290.15	42.0	107.6	315.15
−7.5	18.5	265.65	17.5	63.5	290.65	42.5	108.5	315.65
−7.0	19.4	266.15	18.0	64.4	291.15	43.0	109.4	316.15
−6.5	20.3	266.65	18.5	65.3	291.65	43.5	110.3	316.65
−6.0	21.2	267.15	19.0	66.2	292.15	44.0	111.2	317.15
−5.5	22.1	267.65	19.5	67.1	292.65	44.5	112.1	317.65
−5.0	23.0	268.15	20.0	68.0	293.15	45.0	113.0	318.15
−4.5	23.9	268.65	20.5	68.9	293.65	45.5	113.9	318.65
−4.0	24.8	269.15	21.0	69.8	294.15	46.0	114.8	319.15
−3.5	25.7	269.65	21.5	70.7	294.65	46.5	115.7	319.65
−3.0	26.6	270.15	22.0	71.6	295.15	47.0	116.6	320.15
−2.5	27.5	270.65	22.5	72.5	295.65	47.5	117.5	320.65
−2.0	28.4	271.15	23.0	73.4	296.15	48.0	118.4	321.15
−1.5	29.3	271.65	23.5	74.3	296.65	48.5	119.3	321.65
−1.0	30.2	272.15	24.0	75.2	297.15	49.0	120.2	322.15
−0.5	+31.1	272.65	+24.5	+76.1	297.65	+49.5	+121.1	322.65

TABLE 8 — *Conversion of nautical miles to kilometres*

Nautical Miles	Kilometres	Nautical Miles	Kilometres
1	1.9	20	37
2	3.7	30	56
3	5.6	40	74
4	7.4	50	93
5	9.3	60	111
6	11.1	70	130
7	13.0	80	148
8	14.8	90	167
9	16.7	100	185
10	18.5		

Based on the International Nautical Mile of 1852 m.

TABLE 9 — *Conversion of feet to metres*

Feet	Metres	Feet	Metres	Feet	Metres	Feet	Metres
1	0.30	20	6.1	200	61	2 000	610
2	0.61	30	9.1	300	91	3 000	910
3	0.91	40	12.2	400	122	4 000	1 220
4	1.22	50	15.2	500	152	5 000	1 520
5	1.52	60	18.3	600	183	6 000	1 830
6	1.83	70	21.3	700	213	7 000	2 130
7	2.13	80	24.4	800	244	8 000	2 440
8	2.44	90	27.4	900	274	9 000	2 740
9	2.74	100	30.5	1 000	305	10 000	3 050
10	3.05						

To face page 214 (i)

noving vessel

Apparent force of wind, Beaufort scale	Apparent Speed	40°				50°						Apparent force of wind, Beaufort scale
		15	20	25	30	5	10	15	20	25	30	
1	True di	175	177	177	177	158	171	175	176	176	177	1
	True fo	4	5	6	7	2	3	4	5	6	7	
2	True di	165	169	171	173	115	152	163	168	170	172	2
	True fo	4	5	5	6	2	3	4	5	6	6	
3	True di	146	157	163	167	86	121	145	155	162	165	3
	True fo	4	4	5	6	3	3	4	4	5	6	
4	True di	116	138	150	156	70	97	121	138	148	155	4
	True fo	3	4	5	6	4	3	4	4	5	6	
5	True di	93	115	131	142	64	82	102	119	131	141	5
	True fo	4	4	4	5	4	4	4	5	5	6	
6	True di	77	95	112	125	60	73	88	103	117	127	6
	True fo	5	4	5	5	6	5	5	5	5	6	
7	True di	68	80	95	109	58	68	79	91	103	114	7
	True fo	5	5	5	5	6	6	6	6	6	6	
8	True di	61	71	82	94	56	64	73	82	93	102	8
	True fo	6	6	6	6	8	7	7	7	7	7	
9	True di	57	65	73	82	56	62	69	76	84	93	9
	True fo	8	7	7	7	9	8	8	8	8	8	
10	True di	53	60	66	74	54	60	66	72	78	85	10
	True fo	9	8	8	8	10	9	9	9	9	8	
11	True di	51	56	62	68	54	58	63	68	73	79	11
	True fo	10	9	9	9	11	10	10	10	10	9	
12	True di	50	54	58	63	54	57	61	66	70	75	12
	True fo	11	10	10	10	12	11	11	11	10	10	

12

≥68

tion of

cided,
ved in

parent
r than

Beaufort	90° 5	10	15	20	25	30	100° 5	10	15	20	25	30	110° 5	10	15	20	25	30	Apparent force of wind, Beaufort scale
	8	170	173	175	175	176	159	171	174	175	175	176	162	171	174	175	176	176	1
	2	3	4	5	6	7	2	3	4	5	6	7	2	4	4	5	6	7	
	5	154	162	167	169	171	139	156	163	167	169	171	145	159	164	168	170	172	2
	3	4	4	5	6	7	3	4	5	5	6	7	3	4	5	6	6	7	
	1	139	150	157	161	164	128	143	153	158	162	165	134	148	156	160	164	166	3
	3	4	5	6	6	7	3	4	5	6	7	7	4	4	5	6	7	8	
	1	126	138	146	152	156	119	132	143	149	154	158	127	139	147	153	157	160	4
	4	5	5	6	7	7	4	5	6	6	7	8	4	5	6	7	7	8	
	5	118	129	137	143	148	114	126	135	142	147	151	123	133	141	146	150	154	5
	5	5	6	6	7	8	5	6	6	7	8	8	5	6	7	8	8	8	
	2	112	122	129	136	141	111	121	129	135	140	145	120	129	136	141	145	149	6
	6	6	7	7	8	8	6	7	7	8	8	9	6	7	7	8	9	9	
	9	108	116	123	129	134	109	117	124	130	135	139	118	126	132	136	141	145	7
	7	7	8	8	8	9	7	8	8	8	9	9	7	8	8	9	9	10	
	8	105	112	118	124	129	107	114	120	126	131	135	117	123	128	133	137	140	8
	8	8	9	9	9	9	8	8	9	9	10	10	8	9	9	10	10	11	
	7	102	109	114	119	124	106	112	117	122	127	131	116	121	126	130	134	137	9
	9	9	9	10	10	10	9	9	10	10	10	11	9	10	10	10	11	12	
	6	101	106	111	116	120	105	110	115	119	123	127	115	119	124	128	131	134	10
	0	10	10	10	11	11	10	10	11	11	11	12	10	11	11	11	12	12	
	5	100	104	109	113	116	104	109	113	117	121	125	114	119	123	126	129	132	11
	1	11	11	11	12	12	11	11	12	12	12	12	11	12	12	12	>12	>12	
	4	98	103	106	110	114	104	108	112	115	118	121	114	118	121	124	127	130	12
	2	12	12	12	>12	>12	12	12	>12	>12	>12	>12	12	>12	>12	>12	>12	>12	

7	8	9	10	11	12
0	37	44	52	60	≥68

Apparent force of wind, Beaufort scale	Apparent direction of wind off the bow		170°						180°						Apparent force of wind, Beaufort scale
	Speed of vessel in knots ⇒ 30		5	10	15	20	25	30	5	10	15	20	25	30	
1	True direction, degrees off	179	177	179	179	179	179	179	180	180	180	180	180	180	1
	True force, Beaufort Scale	7	3	4	5	6	6	7	3	4	5	6	6	7	
2	True direction, degrees off	177	175	177	178	178	178	178	180	180	180	180	180	180	2
	True force, Beaufort Scale	8	3	4	5	6	7	8	3	4	5	6	7	8	
3	True direction, degrees off	176	173	175	176	177	177	177	180	180	180	180	180	180	3
	True force, Beaufort Scale	8	4	5	6	7	7	8	4	5	6	7	8	8	
4	True direction, degrees off	174	173	174	175	176	176	177	180	180	180	180	180	180	4
	True force, Beaufort Scale	9	5	6	7	7	8	9	5	6	7	7	8	9	
5	True direction, degrees off	172	172	173	174	175	175	176	180	180	180	180	180	180	5
	True force, Beaufort Scale	10	6	7	7	8	9	10	6	7	7	8	9	10	
6	True direction, degrees off	171	172	173	174	175	175	175	180	180	180	180	180	180	6
	True force, Beaufort Scale	10	7	8	8	9	10	10	7	8	8	9	10	10	
7	True direction, degrees off	170	171	172	174	174	174	175	180	180	180	180	180	180	7
	True force, Beaufort Scale	11	8	8	9	10	10	11	8	8	9	10	10	11	
8	True direction, degrees off	169	171	172	173	174	174	174	180	180	180	180	180	180	8
	True force, Beaufort Scale	12	9	9	10	11	11	12	9	9	10	11	11	12	
9	True direction, degrees off	168	171	172	173	173	174	174	180	180	180	180	180	180	9
	True force, Beaufort Scale	>12	10	10	11	11	12	>12	10	10	11	11	12	>12	
10	True direction, degrees off	168	171	172	173	173	173	174	180	180	180	180	180	180	10
	True force, Beaufort Scale	>12	11	11	12	12	>12	>12	11	11	12	>12	>12	>12	
11	True direction, degrees off	167	171	171	172	173	173	174	180	180	180	180	180	180	11
	True force, Beaufort Scale	>12	12	12	>12	>12	>12	>12	12	12	>12	>12	>12	>12	
12	True direction, degrees off	167	171	171	172	172	173	173	180	180	180	180	180	180	12
	True force, Beaufort Scale	>12	>12	>12	>12	>12	>12	>12	>12	>12	>12	>12	>12	>12	

12

≥68

THE INTERNATIONAL SYSTEM OF UNITS
(Système International d'Unité's)

The International System (SI) consists of seven 'base units' together with two 'supplementary units'. From these are formed others known as 'derived units'. The base of supplementary units, and some of the derived units, have been given names and symbols. The symbols are printed in lower case except where derived from the name of a person; for example m (metre), but A (ampere). Symbols are not pluralized (1 m, 10 m) nor do they take a full stop. The names of the units do not, however, take capitals (except of course at the beginning of a sentence), although they may be pluralized; for example, 1 kelvin, 10 kelvins.

The base units are:

Unit	Symbol	Description
metre	m	the unit of length
kilogram	kg	the unit of mass
second	s	the unit of time
ampere	A	the unit of electrical current
kelvin	K	the unit of thermodynamic temperature, defined as the fraction 1/273.15 of the thermodynamic temperature of the triple point of water.
candela	cd	the unit of luminous intensity
mole	mol	the unit of the amount of a substance which contains the same number of molecules as there are atoms in exactly 12 grams of pure carbon.

The two supplementary units are:

radian	rad	the measure of a plane angle
steradian	sr	the measure of a solid angle

A few of the derived units are:

Quantity	Name of unit	Symbol	Expressed in base units
frequency	hertz	Hz	$1 \text{ Hz} = 1 \text{ s}^{-1}$
force	newton	N	$1 \text{ N} = 1 \text{ kg m/s}^2$
pressure	pascal	Pa	$1 \text{ pa} = 1 \text{ N/m}^2$
work	joule	J	$1 \text{ J} = 1 \text{ N m}$
power	watt	W	$1 \text{ W} = 1 \text{ J/s}$

($1 \text{ newton} = 10^5 \text{ dynes}$, $1 \text{ pascal} = 10^{-2} \text{ millibars}$, $1 \text{ joule} = 10^7 \text{ ergs}$).

NON-SI UNITS

The following non-SI units are in current use in the Met. Office and may be found in publications of the Office.

1. *Pressure*
The millibar or hectopascal is used as the unit of pressure in meteorology. (1 mb = 1 hPa, where h = hecto = 10^2).

2. *Temperature*
The unit Celsius (symbol °C) continues to be used.
Celsius temperature = temperature (in kelvins) minus 273.15 K. Note that the degrees sign (°) is no longer used with K.
A difference in temperature should be expressed by use of the international symbol 'deg' without a qualifying C or K.

3. *Distance*
There is a continuing requirement for ocean distances to be measured in nautical miles (symbol n.mile).
Because the nautical mile varies with latitude an internationally agreed International Nautical Mile is preferred. This has been in use in the United Kingdom since 1970. The International Nautical Mile is defined as 1852 m (6076.12 feet).

4. *Height*
Heights other than cloud heights are expressed in metres. Because of the requirements of aviation the heights of cloud will continue for the time being to be expressed in feet (1 foot = 0.3048 m).

5. *Speed*
The derived SI unit is the metre per second (m/s). However, the World Meteorological Organization recommends the use of the knot for horizontal wind speed for the time being. The symbol kn for knot is recommended to avoid confusion with the symbol for kilotonne and will normally be used in Met. Office publications (1 knot = 1 nautical mile per hour = 0.514 metres per second).

6. *Time*
Units other than SI, such as day, week, month and year, are in common use.

7. *Direction*
Direction is measured in degrees clockwise from north and refers to the true compass, for example 320°, unless magnetic is specifically indicated.

8. *Cloud amounts*
The use of 'okta' for the measurement of cloud amount is authorized by the World Meteorological Organization.

THE INTERNATIONAL AURORA CODE

This code was prepared by the International Union of Geodesy and Geophysics for use by auroral observers during the International Year of the Quiet Sun 1964, and published in the International Aurora Atlas by Edinburgh University Press, 1963.

1. *Auroral Forms*
   G Glow: often the top of an arc on the horizon.
   N Auroral light with unspecified form, usually as seen through breaks in cloud.
   A Arc: like a curving arch, the aurora follows the curvature of the earth.
   B Band: irregular in form.
   P Patch: diffuse like a cloud but with no discernible lower border.
   V Veil: extensive uniform luminosity of diffuse form covering much of the sky.
   R Rays: like searchlight beams.

2. *Qualifying Symbol*
   m Multiple. Multiple forms, not multiplicity of detail: m_3 would mean three off.
   f Fragmentary: a part only of an arc, band or other form, usually after it breaks up.
   c Coronal. Rays converging like spokes of a wheel towards the magnetic zenith.

3. *Structure*
   H Homogeneous: lack of internal structure, uniform brightness.
   S Striated: fine filaments of arcs or bands, often at high altitude.
   R Rayed: addition of rays to other forms, e.g. RA and RB.
   R_1 Short rays, e.g. R_1R, R_1RB, R_1RA: fade rapidly with height.
   R_2 Medium length rays, e.g. R_2R, R_2B, R_2RA: fairly uniform brightness.
   R_3 Long rays, e.g. R_3R, R_3B, R_3A: horizon to zenith; brightness changes with height.

4. *Condition*
   q Quiet: very slow changes in brightness and shape.
   a Active: moves or changes rapidly in a period of the order of one second.
   a_1 Movement of folds or irregularities along the boundaries of bands.
   a_2 Shape of lower border of individual form changes rapidly.
   a_3 Rapid horizontal movement of rays in either or both directions.
   p Pulsating: a fairly rapid, often rhythmical, change in brightness.
   p_1 Pulsating: uniform variation in brightness of a form.
   p_2 Flaming: surges of light usually sweeping upward through forms across the sky.
   p_3 Flickering: large part of a display looks as if lit by flickering flames.

(Continued)

p$_4$ Streaming: irregular change of horizontal brightness along homogeneous forms.

5. *Brightness*
    1 Comparable with the Milky Way: colour not perceived.
    2 Comparable with moonlit cirrus cloud: green colour sometimes visible.
    3 Comparable with brightly lit moonlit cirrus cloud or moonlit cumulus cloud.
    4 Much brighter than 3, and can cast detectable shadows.

6. *Colour Class*
    a Red upper region with green lower region.
    b Red lower border of predominantly green bands.
    c White if faint; green, white or yellow, if a mixture of green, red and blue emissions.
    d Red aurora at high altitude.
    e Red and green irregularly distributed or alternating horizontally along aurora.
    f Blue often in upper region of aurora, purple if mixed with red.

APPENDIX IIB

| REPORT SHEET | THE BRITISH ASTRONOMICAL ASSOCIATION — AURORA SECTION VISUAL AURORAL OBSERVATIONS | | | | | | | | | Completed report to be sent to: | British Astronomical Association Burlington House Piccadilly, London W1V 9AG | | |

SAMPLE REPORT

OBSERVER R.B. Senior Met. Officer STATION OWS Cumulus 57°00'N, 20°00'W Sector Zone 63

YEAR 1990	Time (UTC)	Con-dition	Qualif. symbol	Struct-ure	Form	Bright-ness	Colour	Elevation		Direction	Notes and sketches etc.
Date		MONTH March			NIGHT 25/26			base	top		
25	2000	q		H	G	1	c	0	5	310°–010°	
25	2030	q		H	A	2	c	5	9	300–035	
25	2045	q	f	R_2	B	2	c / b	20	60	000–035	
25	2100	a_1		R_1 / R_1	B / R	2	c / f	10 / 30	20 / 60	320–360 / 010–020	
25	2140	a / p_2	m	R_3	R	2	c / d	10 / 30	70 / 70	320–340 / 350–010	
25	2200	a_3	c	R_3	R	3	a / c	10	110	All sky	
26	0010	p_3	c (Spiral overhead)	R	B	3	c	0	110	260–080	
26	0030	q	m_2	H	P	1 / 2	d / c	20 / 15	50 / 25	320–340 / 000–030	

APPENDIX III

TURBO OBSERVATION WITH NEW EFFICIENCY

To simplify the entering and transmission of a coded meteorological observation, the Royal Netherlands Meteorological Institute (KNMI) has developed a computer program called TURBO1 (Turbo Observation with New Efficiency).

The WMO Commission for Marine Meteorology announced at its Eleventh Session in Lisbon in April 1993, that KNMI had agreed to make available the TURBO1 software and instruction manual, for WMO action to have the system installed on Voluntary Observing Ships equipped with INMARSAT-C. KNMI also agreed to maintain and update the system.

The TURBO1 software requires a DOS personal computer, with at least 410 kb free working memory and a 3.5-inch disk drive. The manual, together with the software, provide all the necessary instructions.

The software has three objectives:

(a)   To compile ships' meteorological reports in standard WMO SHIP code and prepare them for transmission as a standard telex message through the messaging channel of the INMARSAT-C system;

(b)   To store the report on the disk for later retrieval, further quality control and permanent archival for climatological purposes;

(c)   To perform simple quality control on the report prior to its transmission and storage.

The numbers of ships equipped with INMARSAT-C terminals, and INMARSAT Land Earth Stations (LES) able to accept the short code 41 dialling procedure with INMARSAT-C to relay SHIP reports to national Meteorological Services, are expected to increase rapidly with time. There are already sufficient INMARSAT-C LES accepting code 41 ships' reports to provide worldwide coverage.

The software and operating manual are distributed for use by the INMARSAT-C equipped Voluntary Observing Ships of participating countries, and training arranged where necessary. Whenever practicable, the disk is replaced at the end of a ship's voyage. The reports stored on the used disk are extracted, converted for use by all WMO Members and after quality control the compiled marine climatological data are archived for the Marine Climatological Summaries Scheme.

This project is expected to improve the efficiency and accuracy of transmitting and archiving ships' meteorological reports, as well as reduce the cost of these transmissions.

KNMI has also produced a computer program, called TURBO6, to compute surface currents from ship's set and drift, with the aim of distributing it to suitable Voluntary Observing Ships after testing.

APPENDIX IV

WORLD SOLAR ECLIPSES*

For the information of mariners, a schedule of expected solar eclipses, both total and annular up to the year 2015, follows.

Two eclipses during the period will be visible from parts of the United Kingdom:
1. The total eclipse of 11 August 1999, visible from the Scilly Isles, Cornwall and Alderney.
2. The annular eclipse of 31 May 2003, visible from northern Scotland.

Type[1]	Date	Maximum Duration[2]	Maximum Lat[3]	Long[3]	Location
A	29.4.1995	06.37	4° S	79° W	South Pacific, Ecuador, Peru, Brazil
T	24.10.1995	02.11	8° N	113° E	India, Thailand, Cambodia, Sabah
T	9.3.1997	02.50	57° N	130° E	Mongolia, Russia, North Polar
T	26.2.1998	04.09	4° N	82° W	Galapagos, Colombia, Venezuela, Antigua, Montserrat
A	22.8.1998	03.14	3° S	145° E	Sumatera, Sarawak, Melanesia, Pacific
A	16.2.1999	00.40	39° S	93° E	South Indian Ocean, Australia
T	11.8.1999	02.23	45° N	24° E	North Atlantic, Scillies, Cornwall, Europe, Turkey, Iran, India
T	21.6.2001	04.57	11° S	3° E	South Atlantic, Southern Africa
A	14.12.2001	03.53	1° N	130° W	Pacific, ends in Costa Rica
A	10.6.2002	00.23	34° N	178° W	Pacific in entirety
T	4.12.2002	02.04	39° S	60° E	Southern Africa, South Indian Ocean
A	31.5.2003	03.37	67° N	24° W	Scotland, Iceland, Greenland
T	23.11.2003	01.57	72° S	88° E	Antarctica in entirety
A/T	8.4.2005	00.42	10° S	119° W	Pacific, ends in Colombia
A	3.10.2005	04.31	13° N	28° E	North Atlantic, Spain, Africa, Indian Ocean
T	29.3.2006	04.07	23° N	16° E	Atlantic, Africa, Turkey, Black Sea, Russia
A	22.9.2006	07.09	21° S	9° W	Atlantic in entirety
A	7.2.2008	02.12	67° S	150° W	Antarctica, South Pacific
T	1.8.2008	02.27	65° N	72° E	Greenland, North Polar, Russia, Mongolia, China
A	26.1.2009	07.54	34° S	70° E	Indian Ocean, ends in Sumatera
T	22.7.2009	06.39	24° N	144° E	China, Pacific
A	15.1.2010	11.08	2° N	69° E	Ethiopia, Indian Ocean, India, Sri Lanka, China
T	11.7.2010	05.20	20°° N	122° W	South Pacific, ends in Chile
A	20.5.2012	05.46	49° N	176° W	Japan, North Pacific, California
T	13.11.2012	04.02	40° S	161° W	Queensland, Pacific in entirety
A	10.5.2013	06.04	2° N	175° E	Australia, Solomon Islands, Pacific
A/T	3.11.2013	01.40	4° N	12° W	Atlantic, Central Africa
A	29.4.2014	00.00	70° S	131° E	Antarctica in entirety
T	20.3.2015	02.47	64° N	6° W	North Atlantic, Faeroes, North Polar

Notes:
1. T — Total.
   A/T — Annular/Total. Starts and ends as annular, total in the middle.
   A — Annular.
2. Duration of totality or annularity in minutes and seconds of time.
3. Location of maximum eclipse.

---

*Information (September 1994) by courtesy of Mr Sheridan Williams, The Clock Tower, Stockgrove Park, Leighton Buzzard, Bedfordshire LU7 0BG, United Kingdom, to whom any queries or requests for further information should be addressed.

INDEX

226

Printed in the United Kingdom for HMSO
Dd 300828   C25   4/95